CAMBRIDGE COLLEGE Ghosts

Picture credits
W. Heffer & Sons Ltd, Cambridge, and the Master and Fellows of Jesus College, Cambridge: p. 66; W. Heffer & Sons Ltd, Cambridge, and the Master and Fellows of Christ's College, Cambridge: p. 99; The Master and Fellows of Jesus College, Cambridge: p. 73; The Principal and Fellows of Newnham College, Cambridge: pp. 104 and 105; The Master and Fellows of Sidney Sussex College, Cambridge: p. 116.

ISBN 0-7117-0675-1

Jarrold Publishing, Norwich
Printed in Great Britain 1/94

CAMBRIDGE COLLEGE

A gathering of ghosts, ghouls and strange goings-on

by

GEOFF YEATES

To Jen
for putting up with a spare-time writer

Contents

About the author *page 7*

Acknowledgements *8*

Preface *11*

Map *12*

The University, its Colleges and their History 13

Ghosts, Apparitions and the Paranormal 23

Corpus Christi College 33

Girton College 41

Clare College 49

Emmanuel College 55

Jesus College 63

Peterhouse 75

St John's College 84

Christ's College 91

Newnham College 103

Sidney Sussex College 111

Postscript *118*

Bibliography *125*

About the author

Geoff Yeates is an architect by profession and lives with his wife and two teenage children, Mark and Verity, in a south Cambridgeshire village.

After completing his training with a large local authority he went with his family to work in Malawi for eighteen months before moving to South Africa, where they spent more than three years living and working on the world's deepest goldmine. They moved to Johannesburg for a further two years and returned to England at the end of 1986.

He now works predominantly in the field of social housing and is currently preparing a second collection of collegiate ghost stories based at 'the other place', Oxford, while his first novel, a mystery based in the fenlands of East Anglia, gradually takes shape.

Acknowledgements

The original suggestion for a book about the ghosts of Cambridge came from Barbara Russell on an appropriately dark and misty November evening in 1992. I must also thank Barbara in particular for her encouragement in prompting me to pursue the idea seriously, once I had added the word 'college' to her basic ingredients.

I should like to thank Miranda Spicer and her colleagues at Jarrold Publishing without whose support the idea would, in all probability, have stayed an idea.

For permission to use extracts and stories from official college annuals, letters, histories and pictures my sincere thanks go, in the order in which the stories appear, to: the Master, Fellows and Scholars of the College of Corpus Christi and the Blessed Virgin Mary; the Mistress, Fellows and Scholars of Girton College; the Master, Fellows and Scholars of Clare College; the Master, Fellows and Scholars of Emmanuel College; the Master, Fellows and Scholars of Jesus College, Cambridge; the Master and Fellows of Peterhouse; the Master, Fellows and Scholars of St John's College; the Master, Fellows and Scholars of Christ's College; the Principal and Fellows of Newnham College and the Master, Fellows and Scholars of Sidney Sussex College.

I should like to thank Geoffrey Stevenson, a Clare man himself, for permission to use his fascinating article about the apparition at the St John's College 'living' at Souldern, Oxfordshire, details of which are given in the bibliography at the end of the book, and Mr D.N. Clark-Lowe of the Society for Psychical Research for providing me with much helpful information about the Sidgwicks at Newnham and for allowing me access to the society's early records. Thanks are also due to Muriel Brittain, Assistant Keeper of the Records at Jesus College, for trusting me with her signed first edition of Arthur Gray's *Tedious Brief Tales of Granta and Gramarye*, from which excellent collection that college's story is taken in its entirety.

On a more personal note it would be remiss of me not to acknowledge the delightful replies I received to my exploratory letters to the bursars of each college in Cambridge at the end of 1992. Almost without exception the ladies and gentlemen that occupy these busy and demanding positions at the centre of college life went to considerable lengths to provide me with a wide range of information, addresses, possible sources to be pursued and, in some cases, sincere apologies on behalf of their respective institutions for not being suitably equipped with ghostly visitors, as if they themselves had some control over the absentees. Many of them delegated the task to other college officers and their assistants, all of whom responded enthusiastically to my requests for information.

Thus to all the bursars, archivists, historians, librarians, fellows, their assistants and secretaries that replied so courteously and patiently to my numerous letters and telephone calls, I would like to say a personal 'thank you', for without their generous co-operation the project would never have got off the ground.

By way of a postscript to this section I would also like to record for posterity, albeit anonymously, extracts from some of the various apologies I received from those colleges whose ghosts have, I like to think, simply chosen not to reveal themselves yet.

> 'We have not so far acquired the dignity or status associated with a resident ghost. Should one 'materialise' in the next few years it could perhaps feature in the second edition of your book.'
>
> 'I am sorry: we have no ghosts (yet).'
>
> The college 'seems to be singularly bereft of ghostly apparitions. I will ask around and see if any of the older fellows can dredge up anything in their memories but I very much doubt that they will be able to.'
>
> 'I regret that we have no ghosts in our cupboard.'
>
> The college 'has not achieved either the patina or the reputation for trustworthy ghosts.'
>
> 'The historian . . . knows of no authenticated or unauthenticated ghost stories relating to the college. Perhaps the temperament of [the college] is too scientific or just too prosaic.'
>
> 'We cannot unearth any ghostly happenings.'
>
> 'We have not as yet experienced anything spiritual. I shall let you know if it changes!'
>
> 'Should a haunting occur in the near future I will of course let you know.'
>
> And from a small theological college . . .
>
> 'We . . . have no history of any ghosts connected with the property (apart from the Holy Ghost which we very much believe in).'

Preface

There are reputed to be more ghosts in Great Britain than anywhere else on earth, and there are quite probably more books about ghosts as well. I make no apology for adding this compilation to the pile of such works because firstly the subject is invariably fascinating, a cocktail of mystery, suspense, strange goings-on and even stranger characters, and secondly the Cambridge colleges have between them a unique assortment of unusual stories that deserves to be shared. Many of the stories have already been published in college histories and annuals, as well as having been briefly mentioned in *Varsity*, the Cambridge student newspaper, in an interesting feature entitled 'Ghost Town' in March 1989. In most cases, therefore, the chapters that follow embody little in the way of original research on my part, beyond unearthing some of the more obscure details that accompany them.

Some of the stories are detailed accounts of what would probably now be called serial hauntings, with the same ghost seen or heard in the same place by many people over many years. Others are single, fleeting appearances in front of individuals who have had a sufficiently strong belief in what they saw or heard to share their observations and risk ridicule. One or two are unashamedly pure fiction but with authentic settings or characters, and some are not even true ghost stories at all, but qualify for inclusion simply because of their peculiarly ghoulish circumstances.

The book sets out to put the ghosts and ghouls whose stories are told into the context of the locations at which they have occurred. Thus each college's story opens with a note of its location in Cambridge, followed by a summary of its history, as a prelude to the story itself. In some instances the precise locations of the recorded apparitions or events have long since disappeared as the consequence of fire or rebuilding or some other cause, but many remain today more or less as they existed at the time.

For the same reason of context, and by way of a general introduction, I have endeavoured to summarise not only the history of the university in Cambridge but also the history of the study of ghosts and their possible causes. I would, of course, be delighted to receive any comments, corrections or new stories that might be suitable for inclusion in a later edition.

Finally, I have appended a basic bibliography for those wishing to read more on Cambridge and its colleges, as well as on ghosts and paranormal phenomena in general.

Geoff Yeates,
Harston, Cambridge, August 1993

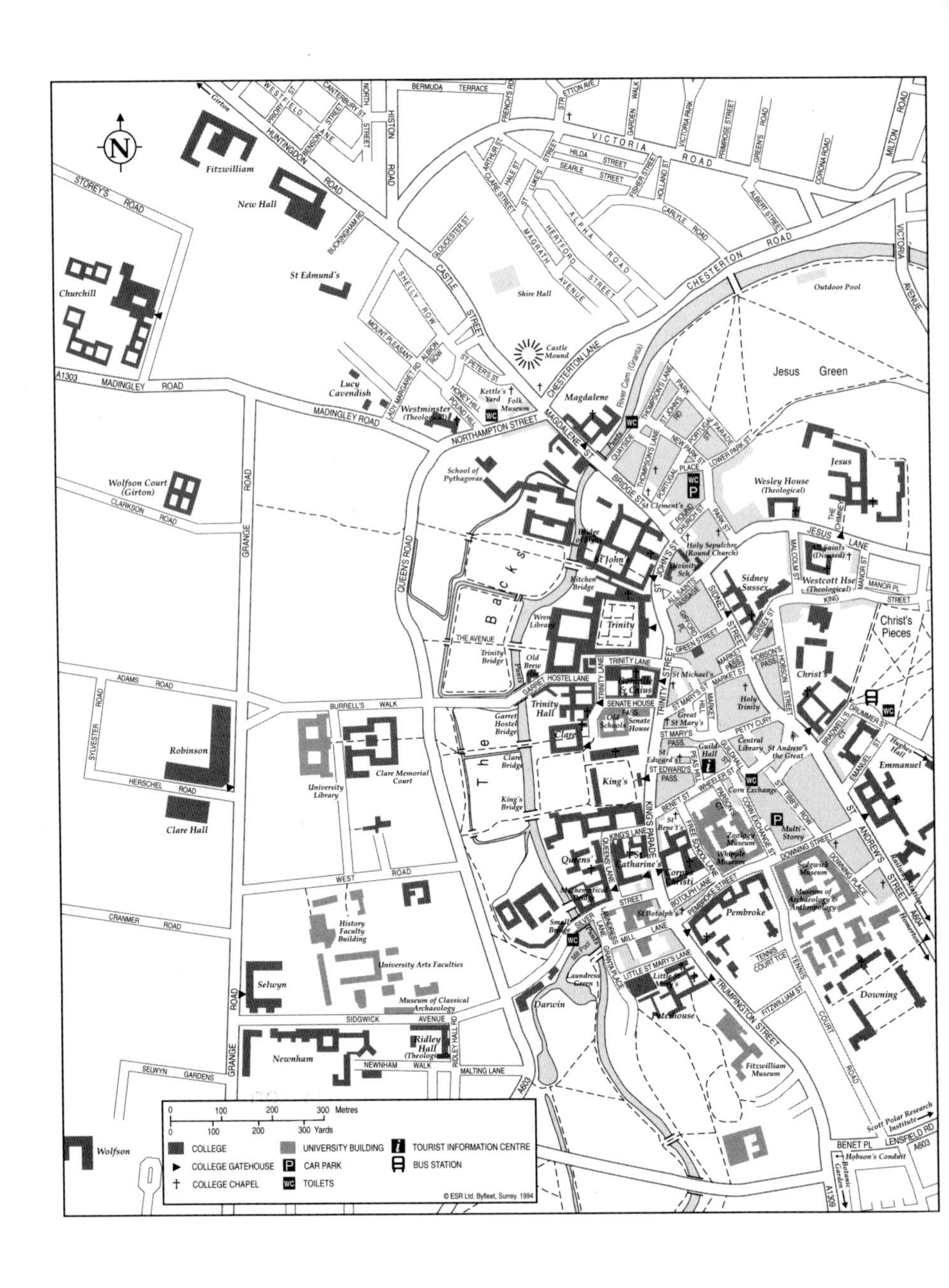
N
Girton
Fitzwilliam
New Hall
HUNTINGDON ROAD
STOREY'S ROAD
BUCKINGHAM RD
St Edmund's
Churchill
A1303
MADINGLEY ROAD
Lucy Cavendish
Westminster (Theological)
Kettle's Yard
Folk Museum
Castle Mound
Shire Hall
Magdalene
School of Pythagoras
Wolfson Court (Girton)
CLARKSON ROAD
GRANGE ROAD
QUEEN'S ROAD
The Backs
Bridge of Sighs
St John's
Kitchen Bridge
Wren Library
Trinity
THE AVENUE
Trinity Bridge
Old Brew Hse
GARRET HOSTEL LANE
TRINITY LANE
Gonville & Caius
SENATE HOUSE
Trinity Hall
Garret Hostel Bridge
Old Schools
Senate House
Clare
Clare Bridge
King's
King's Bridge
Queens'
Mathematical Bridge
St Catharine's
Corpus Christi
Small Bridge
Mill Pool
Laundress Green
Darwin
Little St Mary's
Peterhouse
Pembroke
Fitzwilliam Museum
ADAMS ROAD
SYLVESTER ROAD
BURRELL'S WALK
Robinson
HERSCHEL ROAD
Clare Hall
University Library
Clare Memorial Court
WEST ROAD
CRANMER ROAD
History Faculty Building
University Arts Faculties
Museum of Classical Archaeology
Selwyn
SIDGWICK AVENUE
Ridley Hall (Theological)
RIDLEY HALL RD
Newnham
NEWNHAM WALK
MALTING LANE
SELWYN GARDENS
Wolfson
A603
BERMUDA TERRACE
HISTON ROAD
VICTORIA ROAD
CHESTERTON ROAD
CHESTERTON LANE
River Cam (Granta)
Jesus Green
Outdoor Pool
Jesus
Wesley House (Theological)
JESUS LANE
All Saints (Disused)
Westcott Hse (Theological)
Sidney Sussex
Christ's Pieces
Christ's
Holy Sepulchre (Round Church)
Divinity Sch.
St Clement's
BRIDGE ST
St Michael's
Holy Trinity
Great St Mary's
St Edward's
Guild-Hall
Central Library
St Andrew's the Great
Corn Exchange
Multi-Storey
Zoology Museum
Whipple Museum
St Bene't's
St Botolph's
Sedgwick Museum
Museum of Archaeology & Anthropology
Emmanuel
Hughes Hall
Downing
TRUMPINGTON STREET
TENNIS COURT ROAD
FITZWILLIAM ST
Scott Polar Research Institute
Hobson's Conduit
Botanic Gardens
A1309
A604
Hills Rd Railway Station
0 100 200 300 Metres
0 100 200 300 Yards
COLLEGE
COLLEGE GATEHOUSE
COLLEGE CHAPEL
UNIVERSITY BUILDING
CAR PARK
TOILETS
TOURIST INFORMATION CENTRE
BUS STATION
© ESR Ltd. Byfleet, Surrey. 1994

The University, its Colleges and their History

Cambridge and its university have co-existed for almost eight hundred years but it is not often appreciated that Cambridge had been a thriving market town for well over a thousand years before the first scholars arrived from Oxford in 1209.

Early Days

The area around Cambridge has been inhabited from the neolithic period and the arrival of the Romans in AD 43, *en route* from Colchester to Lincoln, heralded the establishment of a settled community in the shadow of their fortified camp on Castle Hill. The town flourished for nearly four hundred years until the Romans left, to be replaced within a few years by the Angles, Saxons and Jutes from northern Germany.

A second settlement grew up in the area of Bene't Street and Market Hill, but by the end of the seventh century the town was largely deserted. The Danes first visited Cambridge in 875 and quickly realised its potential as an inland port at the head of a river giving access to the sea at King's Lynn. Before long, a wooden bridge had been constructed across the river, near the present Magdalene Bridge, and wharves established along the eastern bank where the older colleges were to develop much later. Cambridge soon became an important trading centre on the main route from East Anglia to the rest of the country. The town's prosperity continued to grow so by 1025 the townspeople could afford to begin the construction of St Bene't's Church, whose Anglo-Saxon stone tower still stands as the oldest building in Cambridge.

The Normans and Beyond

The Normans arrived in the town soon after their invasion of 1066 and built a wooden motte and bailey castle, from which only the mound survives, in an attempt to contain the Saxon outlaws in the fens to the north. Within twenty years, the 'Domesday Book' had

Through this entrance to Old Schools is a building used for university teaching in the fourteenth century

recorded some 400 houses accommodating around 2,000 inhabitants in what was by now a flourishing commercial centre.

Throughout the twelfth century the town's importance as a regional centre increased. Many new churches were founded, including the Church of the Holy Sepulchre – better known as the Round Church – in 1107, and these were followed by several religious houses which were granted rights to hold annual fairs, the fees from which would support them for the coming year. These were popular events to which traders flocked from all over the country. Stourbridge Fair was, for hundreds of years, the largest fair in Europe, lasting for three weeks every September and attracting merchants from far and wide because of its proximity to the river and its ease of access. In years to come, the fair, like many other events and institutions in Cambridge, would fall under the jurisdiction of the university and was not allowed to begin until the Vice-Chancellor had officially proclaimed it open.

The Scholars Arrive

As the thirteenth century dawned, groups of teachers and scholars had established themselves in a small number of centres around Europe, including Paris and Bologna, and were often at odds with the local communities as well as with themselves. With Latin as the common language of Christian learning, scholars could move easily between these centres as they prepared for service in the Church. Oxford had, by this time, become attractive to scholars from Paris because of its relative isolation from direct interference by Church and Court, but this would not last long. In 1209, riots and disturbances within the town and its academic community, culminating in the death of a townswoman, caused the majority of the scholars and their teachers to flee the threat of execution.

Although they dispersed to places as diverse as Reading and Paris, the majority headed for Cambridge. The reasons for this preference are unclear, and it may be simply that the presence of a number of established religious houses in the town provided a degree of spiritual comfort that would more than compensate for the physical discomforts that the scholars would experience in their miserable lodgings.

The Church of the Holy Sepulchre or the Round Church in Sidney Street

The Beginnings of a University

It was not long before groups of scholars were hiring houses, later known as hostels, from the townsfolk. The scholars, often only fourteen or fifteen years old, were difficult to discipline and were frequently the cause of animosity with the town's inhabitants. By 1231 it had become necessary for the King to issue a decree that, amongst other things, all students must be under the control of a 'master'. Despite its troublesome students, the university developed rapidly and within forty years had acquired a chancellor and its own statutes, as well as the beginnings of royal patronage.

In and around Cambridge the Dominicans, Franciscans and Carmelites founded monasteries as the town's prosperity and importance continued to grow. In 1270, no doubt as a consequence of continuing student 'high spirits', the town and the university agreed to share responsibility for maintaining order, but the problem of accommodating scholars in an environment more conducive to civilised learning was not properly resolved until the adoption of the college system.

The Establishment of the Colleges

Having originated in Paris, the idea of providing academic homes for young scholars so that they might be protected from the temptations of taverns and brothels first appeared in England at Oxford, where Merton College was founded by Walter de Merton in 1264. Merton College's statutes eventually came to the notice of Hugh de Balsham, Bishop of Ely, who was to be responsible for founding Cambridge's first college in 1280.

The Bishop decided to place some secular scholars in the Hospital of St John, but after four years, the experiment having been unsuccessful, he bought two houses, beyond the Church of St Peter's-without-Trumpington-Gate, for a master and fourteen 'worthy but impoverished Fellows' who were to live in the college but teach outside. Hugh de Balsham died in 1286 and bequeathed money to the scholars, enabling them to buy more land and erect a dining-hall. They continued to worship at St Peter's and, although the church was rebuilt in 1340 and renamed St Mary the Less, the connection with St Peter's was maintained in the name of this first Cambridge college – Peterhouse.

No new college was founded until Michaelhouse (later part of Trinity College) in 1324, but there followed a further six within thirty years, many of which were subsequently absorbed by other, later foundations. As was the case with Peterhouse, the colleges of the early fourteenth century were endowed foundations, established purely to accommodate teachers, with no resident students and no teaching facilities as such, and it was not until the later years of the century that students joined their teachers in the colleges, following William of Wykeham's innovative ideas at New College, Oxford.

It was towards the end of the fourteenth century that the first university, as distinct from college, buildings were started. Not surprisingly, given the influence of the Church in the early years of scholarship in Cambridge, the first buildings to be completed were the Divinity School and the School of Canon Law, on the site still known as the Old Schools, situated behind the Senate House.

Cambridge had not escaped the horrors of the Black Death in the middle of the century. Indeed, it provided yet another source of conflict between university and town, the former pressing the latter to clean out the open ditches around the town which had effectively become sewers, as scholars and traders alike deserted the town during the hot, summer months. Nor did the Peasants' Revolt of 1381 leave the town unaffected. Two days of rioting led to the public burning of university and college property, as well as the enforced renunciation of their special, and in some cases royally granted, privileges. The revolt was soon suppressed and the privileges restored but the feuding between 'town and gown' continued sporadically for many years.

The Growth of Royal Patronage

Six more colleges followed in the fifteenth century. From the town's point of view, much the most significant event in this period was Henry VI's acquisition in 1441 of the site for his King's College, stretching from Clare College in the north to the Carmelite friars' site (soon to become Queens' College) in the south, and from the old High Street (now King's Parade) in the east to the river in the west. This large area was full of houses, hostels and commercial premises and was criss-crossed by a network of streets and lanes connecting the town centre with the wharves lining the riverbank. To all intents and purposes, and in spite of Henry VI giving the town other land to the north of his site, this signalled the end of river trade in Cambridge. In 1447, Henry acquired the land to the west of the river, across from King's College, which was named 'Kynges college backe sides' on early maps but which later became known, quite simply, as 'The Backs'.

The town's population began to decline towards the end of the fifteenth century. Craftsmen's houses were being gradually taken over by the ever-increasing number of academics who were replacing them as residents, and the character of the town was changing as an inevitable consequence. The town became better known as a centre of learning than a market.

Cambridge's fortunes continued to ebb and flow through the sixteenth century. Its wealth diminished in the early years, only to be restored by an upturn in river trade and the growth of a major market for corn in the town. The Reformation and the dissolution of the monasteries took its toll of the various religious houses,

Downing College, begun in 1807. Architect William Wilkins adopted a neo-Grecian style because George III disapproved of Gothic revival

causing the monks and friars to leave, along with the poorer scholars, and many of the houses were offered to, and taken by, the existing colleges. Six new colleges were established, the largest of which, Trinity, was founded by Henry VIII in 1546 by merging two earlier foundations. This took place only one year after Henry had been presented with a report suggesting that the colleges should go the way of the monasteries. Fortunately for Cambridge and the future of the university, the colleges were allowed to retain their possessions and privileges.

Cambridge's Growing Influence

No new colleges were founded during the seventeenth and eighteenth centuries, but Cambridge's increasingly influential position in the affairs of state and in the fields of science and the arts made it a serious rival to Oxford as a source of intellectual innovation. As such, it continued to attract ever greater numbers of scholars and teachers of the highest calibre, in addition to providing potential benefactors with unparalleled opportunities for contributing to its continuing development. One of these was Sir George Downing, whose grandfather had served both Cromwell and King Charles II, as well as building 10 Downing Street in London. Sir George had left money to found a new college in Cambridge when he died in 1749, but Downing's buildings, in their strikingly different campus setting, were not completed until 1812 because of a series of legal disputes and other difficulties that delayed release of the funds for their intended purpose.

The last third of the nineteenth century saw a further five foundations, including the first British women's colleges in the villages of Girton and Newnham and the relocation of the well-known teacher training college from Homerton in Middlesex to the premises of the former Cavendish College on the southern edge of the town.

Recent Developments

The rapid expansion of higher education during the twentieth century has generated considerable activity within the colleges and the university, particularly in the last thirty years or so. New residential courts have been built by the individual colleges, either as extensions to existing buildings or as remote 'satellites', and new faculty buildings, predominantly lecture rooms, libraries and laboratories, have been developed by the university to accommodate new courses and disciplines. Ten new colleges have been established, five of which are solely for postgraduates undertaking research at the university.

Today, there are over thirty colleges accommodating some 10,000 undergraduates and 3,000 postgraduates, with more than 4,500 research and teaching staff. The continuing strength of the collegiate system, already several hundred years old, is reflected by the admissions procedure for undergraduates, which still requires them to apply to and be accepted by a college for accommodation there, before they are awarded a place on their chosen course of study.

The university's prime role as the provider of teaching and ancillary facilities has, of necessity, grown with the number of students and, in addition to sixty specialist subject libraries and over thirty laboratories, there are ten museums and the university's own library and botanic garden to support the network of lecture theatres. The university, traditionally more impoverished than the fiercely independent colleges, is currently raising funds to assist its continuing expansion within the framework of a ten-year development plan, designed to provide appropriate facilities for the substantially increased student numbers expected by the end of the century.

Cambridge, too, has grown in tandem with the university. It is now an internationally renowned centre of 'high-tech' industry and research in electronics, engineering and medicine, as well as being the base for many important scientific institutions, including the Royal Greenwich Observatory, the British Antarctic Survey and the Scott Polar Research Institute. But in addition, Cambridge is, as it always has been, home to a large population, well over 100,000 at the last census, with little or no knowledge of the intricacies and idiosyncrasies of academic life and for whom the university is as much a hindrance as it is a help to the busy, everyday life of an ancient and prosperous East Anglian market town.

Peterhouse Chapel vestibule, where the Senior Fellow and acting bursar hanged himself in the bell-ropes

Ghosts, Apparitions and the Paranormal

The possibility of an after-life in general and ghosts in particular has fascinated and frightened mankind for thousands of years. Whole cultures have evolved on the fears that these ethereal manifestations from the spirit world engendered in primitive civilisations vulnerable to manipulation by their 'medicine men' and tribal elders. But they are no less frightening or less believable to the sophisticated and technologically advanced societies of the twentieth century. Even now, nobody knows with any certainty whether they exist or not, and, if they do, how they are formed and why they appear. Nor do we have any clear idea why they seem to appear to some people and not to others in the same place at the same time.

Nobody has caught a 'live' ghost and imprisoned it as a tourist attraction in a zoo. Nobody has found, if such a thing could exist, a 'dead' ghost on which to carry out a post-mortem. None has been interviewed on a prime-time television chat show, or been candidly photographed doing something silly with a celebrity in disguise, or achieved its fifteen minutes of fame by exploiting some other pre-arranged media opportunity. Few have ever been caught on film, and those that have are often received with a great deal of scepticism, accompanied by accusations of forgery, fraud and so on.

Nevertheless, for all the lack of hard, reproducible evidence, deemed to be essential to credibility in modern society, ghosts remain as much a part of our culture today as they were in the Middle Ages, when many of the subjects of this book first entered what might be called the spirit world. Furthermore, the religious establishment continues to take ghosts seriously, despite the gradual erosion of many biblical 'facts' into allegories. Many priests within the Church of England and other faiths are regarded as experts in exorcism, authorised to carry out special services to eliminate troublesome spirits in one form or another from the homes of distressed parishioners, albeit with varying degrees of co-operation on the part of the spirit itself.

Spiritualism and Psychical Research

As a religion in its own right, the practice of attempting to communicate with the spirits of the dead – Spiritualism – began almost 150 years ago in the United States. Its adherents claim to be able to contact the spirit world through mediums, facilitating clairvoyant prediction of future events – and clarification of past ones – as well as dialogue with specific spirits at séances, through the use of Ouija boards. Among the early converts to spiritualism in the United Kingdom were such renowned individuals as Sir Arthur Conan Doyle and William Gladstone.

Serious scientific research into the paranormal started in the second half of the nineteenth century, and many of the stories in this book originate in the years leading up to and just after the First World War. The Society for Psychical Research (SPR) was founded in 1882 to investigate and critically assess all aspects of the paranormal, including the claims by spiritualists of their successes in contacting the spirits of the dead. Many of the founding members and early investigators were leading academics and scientists of the time, and their involvement would have added considerably to the credibility of the subject matter they were studying. Less well known is the Ghost Club, which was founded some twenty years earlier in 1862 with a narrower field of study and which lists amongst its more recent members Lord Dowding and the author Dennis Wheatley.

Both these organisations have approached the subject in a controlled, objective and responsible manner and have sought, through experiments designed to eliminate any chance of fraud and collusion, to accumulate evidence that would satisfy even the most sceptical or cynical of observers. It is probably true to say that with the invaluable assistance of modern electronic equipment and recording techniques, both in sound and vision, there is more research under way around the world into the paranormal now than ever before. The objective is, naturally enough, to obtain incontrovertible proof of the existence of ghosts and other psychical and paranormal phenomena which will satisfy the scientific establishment once and for all.

But after over a hundred years of investigation and research we are in essence no closer to formulating definitive answers to the fundamental questions than the Victorian pioneers were. Since we do not yet know what ghosts are made of, we cannot even begin to think about setting up an experiment to create one artificially. And without the opportunity of controlled experiments – and, of course, willing subjects – properly observed and recorded, few scientists are likely to admit openly to their existence.

Types and Categories of Ghosts

Fortunately, those that are prepared to believe in the existence of mechanisms that, under certain circumstances, will create apparitions, be they in the eyes or the minds of the beholders, have not been constrained in their study of the subject by this lack of acceptance from the world of conventional science. In addition to broad classifications defining different types of apparition or haunting, a number of interesting theories have been put forward over the years to try to explain the various phenomena that have been reported. This is not the place to make more than a brief examination of them, so readers wanting to learn more are recommended to two works in particular, first, the fascinating book on the whole subject of the paranormal entitled *The Reality of the Paranormal* by Arthur Ellison and, second, *The Ghost Hunter's Guide* by Peter Underwood, which explores the practicalities of locating and recording ghosts. More details of these are given in the bibliography at the end of this book.

The definitions, and indeed the numbers, of the broad categories into which ghosts have been put vary quite understandably from one expert to another, but mention the subject of ghosts to most people and one category will spring immediately to mind – hauntings.

Traditionally, *hauntings* have taken the form of a moving apparition, often a shadowy figure, which seems completely unaware of the viewer or percipient. It neither hears nor communicates with the percipient in any way and will follow the same track, with the same motions, whenever it is perceived. It is almost as if an 'action replay' is being projected in three dimensions onto the scene by some unseen force, rather than the deliberate and considered motions of a residual 'spirit' with a specific aim in view. One of the more interesting characteristics demonstrated by ghosts adds further weight to the idea of a repeating image. It has long been appreciated that the relative position of an apparition within a building does not take account of any structural alterations that may have been carried out to the building after the apparition's creation. Thus, if an apparition was created on the first floor of an old house and the first floor level was subsequently raised to improve headroom to the ground floor below, the apparition would continue to appear as if the floor had not been changed. In other words, the apparition might appear to subsequent percipients as if it had been cut off at the knees, when viewed either from above the new floor or below it.

This is not so ridiculous as it might seem, in the context of a projected image, when a comparison is drawn with film projection. Assuming that both the shell of the cinema and the projector remain static, as would be the case in the analogy of the old house, and that the screen alone was moved (like the floor), the projected image would no longer appear complete to the eye of the percipient.

Nevertheless, not every potential witness to an apparition actually perceives what those around him or her are perceiving. There are many recorded instances of apparitions, howsoever generated, being seen by some members of a group but not by others when all were present together in the same place. Often, these apparitions have been found to be the cumulative result of traceable natural occurrences such as banging water-pipes, rattling windows and slamming doors, combining with, perhaps, a boring job and an over-active imagination. Once the idea has been suggested by a member of the group that the 'water-hammer' on the floor above may be ghostly footsteps, the more suggestible among the group will tend to seize on any subsequent noise or shadow or sudden draught as irrefutable proof of a 'presence', and so the story feeds upon itself. Psychical researchers called in to lay such 'ghosts' often have to become diplomatic in their interpretation of the cause of sounds and the remedy for their eventual removal to avoid causing unnecessary embarrassment to those involved. In short, such apparitions are based solely upon the power of suggestion. To the people seeing them, of course, the apparitions will have been real enough, but they would not qualify as genuine paranormal phenomena, since they are of a physical, rather than psychical, origin.

Crisis apparitions feature prominently among the other categories of ghosts and are, in many ways, the most convincing of those that have been documented. Typically, an easily recognisable apparition is seen, heard or felt by the percipient at the same time as the person represented by the apparition is in some emotionally critical, perhaps fatal, situation. The percipient then learns at some later date that that person died, possibly thousands of miles away, at the precise moment that the apparition was seen. These cases are convincing because the percipients have shared their experience with a close friend or relative, before any formal notification has been received of the event that ended in crisis. *Post-mortem apparitions* are similar in that they seem mostly to have their origins in some crisis, but their appearance may not occur for several months or even years, and they tend to be less well travelled, generally occurring in the same room, or at least the same house, in which they died.

So What Are Ghosts?

The lack of evidential proof, scientifically assembled and rigorously documented, is of course an impediment to the development of further research but, despite this and the scepticism which inevitably surrounds the subject, one theory which first surfaced in the nineteenth century continues to attract attention from time to time.

It was in 1840 that scientists first became aware that certain people could accurately identify pieces of stone or metal concealed within a cover such as paper or cloth, or even in complete darkness. They were puzzled by the ability displayed by some to identify a wide range of objects separately wrapped in brown paper, and by others who could describe the writer of a letter simply by holding the sealed envelope that contained it. One particularly sensitive individual was able to hold a piece of volcanic rock from Hawaii, wrapped in paper, and describe an exploding volcano in the midst of a blue sea. The same person also successfully identified glacial rock as coming from ice, and saw, in his mind's eye, a picture of outer space when handed a wrapped specimen of meteorite. The scientists concluded that these experiences demonstrated a long-lost human faculty, which they named 'psychometry', and which bore more than a passing similarity to dowsing, if only because of the need for extreme sensitivity of touch.

Although these findings retained their credibility for some years, and indeed created some excitement within the scientific community at the time, they diminished in importance as the then controversial views of Darwin and T.H. Huxley on the origin of Man came to the attention of the world of science in the 1860s. It was almost fifty years before another eminent scientist and SPR member, Sir Oliver Lodge, who had developed an interest in psychical research, brought this theory up to date by suggesting in 1908 that a tragic event could, in effect, be photographed onto the surrounding building fabric, as the direct result of the intensity of the emotions felt at the time.

Electromagnetism, Water and Other Natural Phenomena

Sixteen years later, in 1922, a Cambridge undergraduate called T.C. Lethbridge saw what he later realised was a ghost resembling a college porter, except that, in place of the traditional porter's red coat, the apparition seemed to be wearing a grey coat, as if it were part of a black-and-white photograph. The significance of this did not immediately strike Lethbridge, and he remained at Cambridge for many years, becoming keeper of Anglo-Saxon antiquities at a university museum. In 1957, he left Cambridge and retired to Devon with his wife, intent upon pursuing his interest in archaeology. But it was not long before a series of unusual and unconnected events brought his earlier experience of a ghost back to mind, and he became absorbed in trying to draw together several diverse strands that might be woven into a single, cohesive theory to explain the interrelationships of a number of distinct phenomena.

Lethbridge and his wife began to notice that certain places they visited made them feel badly depressed, but that this depression lifted as quickly as it had descended when they moved away from that place. By trial and error, they established that these areas were localised and that they could, in effect, step in and out of the patches of gloom at will. Over several years this happened on many occasions, and in many different locations, and, each time, investigation revealed that something untoward had happened in each affected place. In one, the body of a suicide victim was found concealed in a forest a few days after the Lethbridges had experienced feelings of gloom and depression as they walked close by; in another, they had sensed something evil on a beach at the foot of a cliff, only to feel a strong, almost irresistible, urge to jump off the edge of the cliff above when they climbed up there. Nine years after they first noticed these feelings a man committed suicide from that same spot.

Lethbridge had in the meantime begun to identify water as a key element in his studies. The discovery that underground watercourses produce minute local changes in the earth's magnetic field explained much, as many of his own experiences had been close to either water or areas of significant dampness. In short, Lethbridge began to believe that running water was accompanied by a naturally generated field of static electricity that could record the extreme emotions created by, for example, a suicide attempt. It had been known for some time that the human body is also surrounded by a mild electrical field which would be the obvious source of these emotional signals; conversely, it would also, of course, be the means of receiving the same signals, transmitted by the static field.

Lethbridge continued to develop his ideas, and those of his predecessors, into other connected topics as he sought one comprehensive theory of the paranormal. These included dowsing, which also depends upon sensitivity to the electrical fields associated with water, and the scientific study of the motion of pendulums of certain lengths. Although not a spiritualist, he had become convinced at the time of his death in 1971 that there are other types of existence beyond the world we currently experience and other energy sources available to human beings which we have not even begun to consider, let alone understand.

The fundamental question – what are ghosts? – still does not have a definitive answer, but it probably is getting closer. The idea of images of real life, as distinct from stylised paintings, being preserved in some static form for future use was inconceivable to the Victorians, until photography was developed. The same can be said of the moving images of the cinema, and of radio in the early years of this century. T.C. Lethbridge would have been in his thirties before the marvel of television thrilled the nation.

We now take satellite broadcasts and video-recorders for granted in their ability to transmit and receive images over great distances and then store them indefinitely, for us to view whenever we wish.

It will be recalled that the classic haunting ghost has been variously described as an 'action replay' and as a 'black-and-white photograph'. If Lethbridge's views about the retention of emotionally generated images in electrical fields are considered alongside these descriptions of ghosts, it is not stretching the imagination too far to equate Lethbridge's perceptions of depression and gloom with what amounts to the reception of projected images from the 'charged' places. In other words, what he felt as nervous sensations, others might have seen as ghosts.

The concept of projection itself is not as strange as it may seem. One technological advance, and there are many, of benefit to researchers into the paranormal is the increasing sensitivity of measuring equipment. Technical and health-orientated magazines have in recent years been publishing articles on the affects of electromagnetism on the human body's systems, themselves electrically based, and there is concern that the rapidly increasing use of electrical goods within society may become yet another health hazard to be avoided. It is known that all naturally occurring materials such as stone, wood and, of course, water have extremely low, but now measurable, magnetic fields. It is reasonable to assume that buildings constructed with these materials will also produce such fields.

Radio and television broadcasts depend upon the atmosphere's electromagnetic properties for the transmission of signals which are, to all intents and purposes, projected to receiving aerials or dishes. Visible light is itself a small part of the electromagnetic spectrum along with X-rays, infra-red and ultra-violet light. We are surrounded by projected images but, with the sole exception of visible light, we cannot interpret them directly ourselves because we need the right receiver to be compatible with the transmitter and its signal.

Professor H.H. Price, a well-known psychical researcher in the first half of this century had suggested that a building's own magnetic field might be minimally altered because of these highly emotional events, which he called a 'psychic charge'. Thus, if human beings, experiencing some violently stressful set of emotions as in a suicide or a murder, could become the unwitting 'transmitters' of some faint signal, which endured in the building as a 'psychic charge', there is, of course, no reason why other human beings should not also become the 'receivers' in precisely the same way as has been discussed earlier in connection with the static electrical field of running water. In receiving the signal from such a charge, therefore, the percipient 'sees' an apparition of the person who first transmitted the charge and believes it to be a ghost.

Water is, of course, invariably present in the structure and fabric of old buildings in the form of what is generally called rising damp, even though, as often as not, it has fallen in through the roof. This may explain why so many ghosts and apparitions are found in such places but it remains to be seen, or perhaps perceived, if further research into the combined effects of water and naturally occurring electrical and magnetic fields is more successful in convincing the scientific establishment of the existence of ghostly phenomena than has been the case to date.

.... and Finally

In drawing this summary of 'the story so far' to an end for the time being, one modern scientific innovation deserves mention and that is holography. This is a photographic technique that creates three-dimensional images with mirrors and projectors by splitting a laser beam into two beams, each beam carrying complementary 3-D information about the object. These are known as holograms, and they are purely apparitions, just like ghosts. They appear to be solid and to have substance, and they can be made to move and to repeat their movements, although only to the extent of the photographically recorded image. What is even more interesting is that sound can also be treated holographically, and it is currently suspected that bats may navigate by this means.

The ghosts and 'ghoulish' events that are the subject of this book fall into more than one of the categories described, often at the same time. No attempt has been made here to sort the various apparitions into appropriate pigeon-holes – that is for the reader to consider at his or her leisure. Nor has the authenticity of the stories been tested by sitting in wait in dark and dingy college rooms and damp gardens. At least one of the colleges featured does not have any recorded apparitions at all, or indeed any stories, but the nature of the incident described is such that, like many other colleges, it certainly deserves them. I can only assume, in cases like these, that the ghosts themselves have not, so far, felt it appropriate to broadcast their presence and that the receivers' tuners are not quite on the same wavelength as the transmitters – yet.

Corpus Christi College

Corpus Christi is both one of the smallest and one of the oldest colleges in Cambridge University, with some 230 undergraduates. The college sits at a slight bend on the east side of Trumpington Street, with the north-west corner of New Court constricting both footpath and roadway, almost opposite the open Principal Court of St Catharine's College. To the north is the Anglo-Saxon Church of St Bene't, the oldest surviving building in Cambridge, which has long been associated with the college, to the extent that Corpus was commonly known as Bene't College until the new entrance from Trumpington Street was created as part of New Court in 1827. Immediately south of New Court the mostly fourteenth century St Botolph's Church faces bespoke tailors and high-class grocers, and barely escapes the heavy traffic, generated by the near-by Lion Yard shopping centre, as it moves east along Silver Street and turns south into Trumpington Street past the Pitt Building, once the home of the Cambridge University Press. The eastern boundary is formed by the tortuously narrow Free School Lane, formerly Luthburne Lane, against which are the parts of Old Court that have long been the resting place of the Corpus Ghost.

A Brief History

The College of Corpus Christi and the Blessed Virgin Mary was founded in 1352. It is unique amongst the colleges of Cambridge and Oxford in having been founded by the townspeople of the two guilds named in its full title, as distinct from the aristocracy and clergy who were responsible for so many of the early colleges. The Guild of Corpus Christi had acquired land in Luthburne Lane, south of St Bene't's Church, between 1342 and 1346 but it was not until 1352 that it united with the Guild of the Blessed Virgin Mary and founded the college with a licence procured under royal charter from King Edward III by Henry, Duke of Lancaster, and an alderman of both guilds.

Building work started immediately on what is now known as Old Court, the first of the many Cambridge 'courts' or quadrangles, but was not completed until twenty-five years later. Corpus Christi has been associated with St Bene't's since 1353 when the church was conveyed by the guilds to the college. St Bene't's, built in the early eleventh century, passed through many hands before the guilds acquired it in 1350 from Sir Giles d'Argentyn. It served as the college chapel until the late sixteenth century when the college built its own to the south of Old Court. Contributors to the costs of the new chapel, demolished in 1823 for an even newer one, included Queen Elizabeth I and Sir Francis Drake.

The south-east corner of Old Court – the old Master's Lodge – where W.S. Moule had his rooms

Old Court has been continuously inhabited since its completion in 1377, longer than any other building in the university. Its appearance has changed little in that time. The buttresses and attic rooms with their dormer windows were added during the sixteenth century, and the south-west corner was remodelled during the construction of New Court.

New Court was built between 1823 and 1827 by William Wilkins, better known for his competition-winning design for

Downing College, and is regarded as an important example of the Gothic Revival. To make way for it, the Elizabethan chapel was demolished and replaced, the old hall was converted to kitchens and a new library was built to house the priceless collection of medieval manuscripts assembled by a former master and Archbishop of Canterbury, Matthew Parker. In addition to works around the court itself, a new hall and Master's Lodge were developed to the east. Wilkins was so pleased with his work here that he asked to be buried in the chapel.

Notable past scholars at Corpus Christi include the dramatists Christopher Marlowe and John Fletcher, Sir Nicholas Bacon, Elizabethan statesman and father of Francis Bacon, and Thomas Cavendish who, between 1585 and 1588, was the second Englishman to sail around the world. Two years before the death of Francis Bacon in 1628, Henry Butts, a doctor of divinity, became Master of Corpus Christi. He was also Vice-Chancellor of the University and, like his predecessors, lived in the old Master's Lodge which occupied the south-east corner of Old Court, next to the then college hall.

The Corpus Ghost

Dr Butts had only been master for six years when he committed suicide on Easter Day, 1 April 1632 by hanging himself in the Master's Lodge with a noose made from a handkerchief. But Dr Butts, although the most likely, is not the only candidate to consider for the identity of the Corpus Ghost.

In the last third of the seventeenth century the master was Dr William Spencer, rector of Landbeach near Cambridge. His daughter had become embroiled in an affair during this period, and opinions differ as to whether it is the daughter or her lover that is responsible for the hauntings reported below, but the most imaginative, if not gruesome, version suggests that the ghost is that of the lover. Legend has it that the couple were disturbed in the midst of a clandestine meeting, so the lady promptly hid her lover in a cupboard where, no doubt to her considerable inconvenience, not to mention his, he suffocated. There is no record of what happened to the daughter, or indeed to the cupboard and its contents, but it seems likely that the latter two disappeared when the old Lodge was converted into sets of rooms for dons and undergraduates in 1825, following the Revd John Lamb's occupation of Wilkin's new Master's Lodge in New Court the previous October.

There had long been a tradition within the college that the upper rooms in this corner of Old Court, not far from the kitchens, were haunted, but there is no surviving record of any hauntings until 1883, when Mr W.S. Moule came up as a freshman.

W.S. Moule had rooms in what had been the old Master's Lodge, on the same staircase as his uncle, Mr Charles Moule, who had become Senior Fellow in 1879. Charles Moule had often been troubled by mysterious noises in his rooms but was reluctant to talk about them in later life, perhaps because on one occasion, according to undergraduate gossip, he had been so consumed with terror that he felt compelled to crawl out of the rooms in broad daylight on his hands and knees. W.S. Moule, who was later to become a missionary in China and Archdeacon of Zhejiang (Chekiang), was familiar with these occurrences and remembered hearing loud bangs, like the falling of a trapdoor, or perhaps, more romantically, the hurried slamming of a cupboard door.

He recalled another occasion involving a friend, Eric Lewis, who occupied an adjoining set of rooms. One night Lewis became so disturbed by the mysterious noises that he left his bedroom to take refuge with W.S. Moule and was only calmed down by prayer. Others within Corpus were convinced of the existence of a ghost, most notably two of the college chefs of the period, Porcheron and Body, and it was said at the time that no servant would remain alone in the kitchens at night for fear of being confronted by a terrifying apparition.

Several years passed with little more than occasional footsteps and unaccountable rappings on the walls, and it was not until the Michaelmas term of 1903 that events took a distinct turn for the worse. The noises became louder and more frequent, and an anonymous undergraduate was once woken in the dead of night by thunderous knocking, accompanied by the violent shaking of the wash-stand at the foot of his bed. But, as on all previous occasions, there was no sighting and thus no clue as to the identity of the apparition.

The college's residents did not have to wait long before a visible manifestation occurred, for it was in the following Easter term of 1904 that Llewellyn Powys, an undergraduate with rooms in Old Court opposite those which were supposed to be haunted, had the dubious distinction of being the first man to see the Corpus Ghost.

The main entrance gate of Corpus Christi College

Powys had returned to his rooms at about three o'clock one afternoon to do some work. As soon as he sat down at his desk to commence his studies, he found himself experiencing a curious uneasiness around him which made it impossible for him to concentrate on his work. He felt inexplicably drawn to the window and, looking across the court, noticed the head and shoulders of a man leaning out of the window of the upper set of rooms opposite. To Powys' surprise, he could not recognise the man, who had long hair, and who seemed to be glaring down at him whilst remaining completely motionless within the opening. Powys stood at the window for a full three minutes, before hurrying to his bedroom in the belief that he would have a better view. But by the time he arrived at the bedroom window the stranger had vanished. Powys was by now thoroughly excited and rushed across to the rooms opposite. Finding the door locked, he knocked repeatedly and called out, but there was no reply from within. That evening, he discovered to his amazement that Milner, the undergraduate occupying the rooms concerned, had been out for the whole afternoon. Furthermore, it was impossible for anyone to have been in his rooms between the time of his departure at two o'clock and the arrival of his bedmaker at half-past six.

Over the following months the ghost became more troublesome and the disturbances more frequent. An undergraduate, who occupied the rooms below Milner's set, awoke at about five o'clock one morning to find himself in the presence of a white figure standing beside his bed. The figure remained motionless for some minutes, before disappearing through the closed door to the sitting-room. The young man, thoroughly unnerved by this experience, dressed and left his rooms immediately. On a later occasion in the same rooms the mysterious noises became so loud and so intimidating one night that the young man went out and persuaded a friend to keep him company. When they returned, the rooms were silent and empty but the friend, seeing the strain on his colleague's face, invited him to sleep in his sitting-room. The invitation was declined but they did return to the friend's rooms and talked for some time.

The young man made his way back to his own rooms in due course with the intention of going to bed, but as soon as he opened the door to his set of rooms, he saw the ghostly figure of a man standing by the fireplace. Not surprisingly, he hurried back to his friend's rooms in a state of considerable alarm and spent the rest of the night on his sitting-room sofa. The following morning the undergraduate approached the college authorities and demanded to be moved to another set on a different staircase. His rooms remained empty for some time afterwards.

Elsewhere in Old Court, A.N. Wade, an undergraduate ordinand, occupied a set of haunted rooms in which noises continued to be heard every night for some months. Together with two friends, J.W. Capron, an ordinand at King's College, and J.R. (later Sir Shane) Leslie, a member of the Cambridge Psychical Research Society, Wade decided in October 1904 to attempt to exorcise the Corpus Ghost.

Capron took with him a phial of holy water and Wade carried a crucifix. These two, with Leslie, entered the haunted room which was in total darkness except for the meagre light from a dying fire. The exorcism began with them all kneeling to recite the Lord's Prayer, following which Capron, raising the crucifix above his head, called upon the three persons of the Trinity to command the spirit to appear. It was then seen by both Capron and Wade. They later described it as appearing in the form of a mist about a yard wide, which slowly assumed the shape of a man shrouded in white, with what appeared to be a gash in his neck. Capron and Wade watched as it moved slowly around the room and attempted to approach the apparition as they held the crucifix out in front of them. As Capron sprinkled the phial of holy water about the room, they were hurled back by what seemed to be an invisible force. Leslie had not been able to see the figure initially but remembered later experiencing his hair rising and a prickling in his scalp.

All three then saw the ghost, framed in the open doorway. It had a strangely menacing appearance and seemed to be cut off at the knees. As they gripped each other tightly, the ghost disappeared, and Capron, believing that it had moved to the room above, led the trio as they charged up the stairs and into the room occupied by a medical student who was both a pronounced atheist and a sceptic of the supernatural. The student had been calmly reading as the three burst in. Capron advanced with the crucifix uplifted in front of him towards one of the darker corners of the room as the student suddenly darted in front of him. Before Capron could shout a warning, the student had collapsed on the floor, murmuring that he felt very cold.

The commotion accompanying these events inevitably attracted other undergraduates, who came rushing in to the room, but the ghost had already vanished by the time they arrived. The three participants were led away in a state close to exhaustion, and it was left to the college authorities to deal with the aftermath.

The affair was hushed up as far as possible by the college, who closed the haunted rooms temporarily, as there was naturally some considerable reluctance on the part of many junior members of the college to occupy them. It was left to an American undergraduate named Tabor to make an offer to occupy one of the sets of hurriedly vacated rooms, rent free, and so restore both the dented reputation of the staircase and an appropriately calm atmosphere.

This series of events caused quite a stir at the time and on Sunday afternoons attracted many visitors who would lean on the railings that then surrounded Old Court, pointing animatedly at the evil spot. The opportunity to satisfy the visitors' curiosity, as well as providing themselves with some entertainment, was not lost on the students, who, after slipping into a handy surplice, would wave their arms mischievously from behind the windows.

The incident was forgotten after a time, no doubt to the great relief of the college authorities, and although it remained a talking point for some years, there have been no further reports of the Corpus Ghost having been seen or heard again. As with all such instances, there was more than one contemporary sceptic inclined to attribute the whole affair to a play of nerves, with an element of hoaxing, and there is, of course, no conclusive evidence of an apparition, one way or the other. But there is one intriguing fact worthy of mention on which to close the story of the Corpus Ghost.

The ghost, in its clearest manifestation, appeared to be cut off at the knees as it lingered in the open doorway. There is more than one possible cause for this, as there is for the reported gash on its neck. It might indeed have been just that, but it might equally have been a dark handkerchief rather than a gruesome wound. The three exorcists, as undergraduates, are extremely unlikely to have been aware of the existence of a letter written by an unidentified Fellow of Corpus Christi on 4 April 1632, three days after Dr Butts' suicide. The letter describes the circumstances surrounding this tragic event, and, in particular, how 'he tied the handkerchief about the superliminare of the portal . . . which was so low that a man could not go through it without stooping; and so wilfully with the weight of his body strangled himself, his knees almost touching the floor.'

Girton College

Girton is more than two miles to the north-west of the city centre straight up the Huntingdon Road, more prosaically known as the A604, on the line of the old Roman road from Colchester to Lincoln. The extensive and immaculate grounds, unlike those of the older and more central colleges, include sports fields in the fifty acres situated at the southern tip of the village of Girton, from

Emily Davies Court and the ancient burial ground haunted by a Roman centurion

which the college took its name. The site is full of trees, and the college makes full use of them by hiding away from the constant stream of traffic heading relentlessly to and from the city centre, so that it is difficult to see many of the buildings from the road.

A Brief History

Girton was the first women's college to be founded but the second to be established in Cambridge, having moved to its present site in 1873, two years after Newnham College had opened.

The entrance to Girton College and the gatehouse tower

This quirk in timing originated with the establishment in 1869 of a college for women in Hitchin, Hertfordshire, following two years of preparation by a committee of eminent men and women who were concerned at the lack of higher education opportunities then available to women.

The college first opened in October 1869 at Benslow House,

Hitchin, with five students. The lecturers, mostly young gentleman volunteers, travelled twenty-six miles from Cambridge to give their lectures and then travelled twenty-six miles back again. The travelling alone would have taken them about three hours in those days, so when the lease on Benslow House was coming up for renewal a decision was taken to move the college to Cambridge and thus remove some of the more obvious disadvantages of being so far away from the university.

Land was acquired in Girton, which was considered to be close enough for male lecturers to visit with ease and far enough away from the centre to deter male students from doing the same. Building work started quickly, and in October 1873 the ladies of Girton moved from Hitchin into their new accommodation.

The early buildings were designed by Alfred Waterhouse, architect of the Natural History Museum in London, and used his customary red brick and terracotta in a mock Gothic style. Outwardly the buildings were typical of older college plans with their enclosed courts but Waterhouse introduced the novel idea of providing the living accommodation on horizontal corridors rather than the traditional vertical staircase arrangement that had survived for centuries, despite its inherent inconvenience for residents.

The great majority of the buildings was completed within the first thirty years, and their grouping presents a uniformity of character and style not found in the older colleges, with full use being made of the generous space available within the site. Apart from the completion of the south-east and south-west ranges of Woodlands Court, completed in 1931 by Waterhouse's grandson Michael, whose father Paul built the Tower Wing in 1887, little more has been carried out in Girton itself.

The library was extended in 1967, making it one of the larger college libraries in the university with over 75,000 books, and a satellite of the college, Wolfson Court, finished in 1969, was built in Clarkson Road, close to the city centre, as a celebration of Girton's centenary in Cambridge. One hundred students are accommodated here in addition to the three hundred at the main site.

Girton admitted male students for the first time in 1977, almost thirty years after gaining full collegiate status in 1948, when

The Taylor Knob, built in memory of Miss E.H. Taylor

Queen Elizabeth the Queen Mother became the first woman to be awarded a Cambridge degree, an honorary doctorate in law.

The Ghosts of Girton

Girton has two ghost stories which, for an institution of such comparative youth, puts many of the medieval foundations to shame. There is, however, little in the way of contemporary reports and documentary evidence to provide any real certainty as to the identities of either the percipients or the apparitions, or for that matter the number of visitations witnessed over the years by students and staff. The tales that follow have therefore been handed down by word of mouth since the end of the nineteenth century and are now appearing in print, as far as is known, for the first time.

The first tale concerns a ghost of considerable antiquity. The setting was an area of rough ground in front of one of the earliest buildings which, in 1881, was being cultivated for the laying of a lawn. During the preparatory excavations a large number of burials were found which were identified as mostly Saxon, but with a few Roman remains as well, and the inevitable, if unpleasant, conclusion was that Girton College had been built on the site of an ancient cemetery, dating from the time when the Huntingdon Road had been a much used Roman thoroughfare.

The excavations were extended in 1886 and detailed records maintained in notebooks which are kept in the college's archives. Two Girtonians, one of whom was an assistant curator at the university's Museum of Archaeology and Ethnology, were able to use the material in writing a book entitled *The Anglo-Saxon Cemetery at Girton College, Cambridge* which was published by the University Press in 1926. Unfortunately, neither the contemporary notebooks nor the later publication contain any reference to the ghost.

There was only one known sighting at the time and that was by a student strolling in the grounds at dusk in the vicinity of the excavations who said that she had caught sight of a figure resembling a Roman centurion as it walked, or possibly marched, along the edge of the workings.

Perhaps it was coincidence – an ancient spirit disturbed, quite literally, by the excavations and doomed to walk the fields of Girton at dead of night – or perhaps it was simply the over-active imagination of an impressionable young lady of the time who was not a little nervous at being so close to an ancient and partly excavated burial ground in the gathering darkness. Nevertheless, there have been no further sightings of a Roman centurion reported at the college, unlike the second brief story of the Grey Lady which, although it too was only seen once, did at least have the audacity to appear simultaneously to a group of ladies.

Girton College's Grey Lady Staircase

It was around 1876 that a small block known as the Taylor Knob was built in a remote corner of the college site with a benefaction from Thomas Taylor and his wife in memory of their daughter, Miss E.H. Taylor, who had been accepted for admission to Girton but who had died suddenly before she could take up her place.

Shortly thereafter a number of students claimed that they had together seen an apparition in the form of a grey lady. The apparition had taken place on the spiral staircase in the Taylor Knob and the young ladies, no doubt being familiar with the tragedy, were convinced that it was that of Miss Taylor who, having been so cruelly deprived of her earthly chance to pass through Girton, seemed to be taking a more ethereal, and less laborious, route through the college.

The story proved popular with a succession of resident housemaids who handed it down over many years but there were those in the college who were always inclined to be sceptical, and possibly for good reason. The early years of Girton, as in the great majority of late Victorian buildings and institutions, was a time of feeble paraffin lights, which struggled with little success to illuminate the corridors and staircases and which were extinguished every evening at ten o'clock precisely. Any students moving about late at night thus had nothing but their own flickering candles to light their way and, no doubt, an assortment of shadows to keep them company on their travels. The sceptics, naturally, insisted that the Grey Lady was nothing more sinister than a wakeful student wearing a flowing grey dressing-gown as she made her way either to or from the kitchen on the middle floor of the building for a cup of tea.

Who was closer to the truth at the time will never be known but old Girtonians still know those spiral stairs as the Grey Lady Staircase. But what of the Grey Lady herself? The one certainty is that there were no further reports of her activities once the college had installed electric lighting – perhaps, faced with competition from the massed ranks of hundred-watt light bulbs, she simply gave up the ghost.

Gatehouse to Clare College on Trinity Lane

Clare College

Clare College is tucked away behind the Old Schools site to the east of the Backs, between Trinity Hall to the north and King's College to the south. Its compact frontage to Trinity Lane, just across from King's College Chapel, belies its true size as one of the larger colleges with over 500 junior members, because the main site at Memorial Court is some 300 metres to the west, on the far side of Queens' Road next to the monumental pile of the University Library. The pedestrian link between the two sites is one of the more attractive routes in the city and includes the picturesque but slightly sagging Clare Bridge which dates from 1628.

A Brief History

Clare is the second oldest of the colleges and has probably had more names than any other. It was founded in 1326 by Richard de Badew, the University Chancellor, as University Hall but was a poor foundation and could only support two chairs, one of which was for the master. Having inevitably run into financial difficulties after a few years, it was effectively rescued by Elizabeth de Burgh, Countess of Clare and granddaughter of Edward I, in 1338 when she supplied sufficient endowments for the college to be refounded as Clare House. Before long the name was changed to Clare Hall, and changed again to Clare College in 1856.

The college's original buildings were comparatively generous in the accommodation they provided. In addition to the master and nineteen fellows, ten poor boys were to receive free education and lodging. The buildings were not of the best construction because, although a fire caused considerable damage in 1521, they were so dilapidated at the end of the sixteenth century that the college decided to replace them on an adjacent site, closer to the river and further away from King's College Chapel.

The seventeenth century saw much building work completed despite a pause for the duration of the Civil War from 1642 to 1652. During this period much of the stone that had been obtained for the works was taken by Parliamentarian troops to strengthen what remained of Cambridge Castle. It should be added that the Lord Protector, Oliver Cromwell, who was perhaps sympathetic to the plight of the colleges as he was a Sidney man himself, did eventually pay for the stone that was removed.

The west side of Old Court from Clare Bridge over the River Cam

By 1715 the whole of Old Court had been completed in an elegant classical style which was almost palatial in comparison to many of the earlier college buildings elsewhere in the town. In 1769 the chapel was completed, and no further projects were undertaken until Memorial Court, commissioned in memory of college members who died in the First World War and designed by Sir Giles Gilbert Scott, was finished in 1934.

Twenty years later the same architect built the neighbouring Thirkhill Court to the south, since which time a new hostel block has been built on Castle Hill and the library completed in 1985 within Memorial Court itself.

The Skeleton in the Cupboard

Clare College does not have a ghost story in the traditional sense, but it does have a most unusual benefaction which, partly because of a particularly ghoulish direction within the benefactor's will, more than compensates for the unfortunate lack of any apparitions and might even have helped ward them off in the first place.

The college history, in its section on eighteenth century literary and artistic alumni, sums them up as being for the most part 'rakes and eccentrics'. There can be little doubt that the benefactor in question, Dr Robert Greene, although by no means a rake, was an eccentric above and beyond the call of duty, whose sole, but enduring, claim to fame proved to be the unwitting inspiration for one of the more ghoulish expressions in the English language, 'the skeleton in the cupboard'.

Greene was born in Tamworth, Staffordshire, around 1678. His father was a mercer, or cloth merchant, and Greene was sent to Cambridge at the age of seventeen, where he was admitted to Clare in October 1695. He became a Fellow in 1703 and was presented, in the same year, to the Parish of Everton, near Sandy in Bedfordshire, where he remained vicar until his death in 1730. Greene later became Dean of the college and took his responsibilities seriously in both college and parochial life.

Greene had not been a Fellow for long when he began to publicise his strange views on a range of subjects. He denied the existence of vacuum, questioned the conventional theory of gravity and insisted, through some quirk of his own mathematical misunderstanding, that the circle could be squared, although none of his contemporaries and successors seems to have known quite what he meant by such an obscure remark.

In addition, he was violently opposed to Sir Isaac Newton's revolutionary scientific theories, which he believed subverted religion. Newton died only three years before Greene and, as a Fellow of Trinity College and professor of mathematics at Cambridge, he may well have been aware of Greene's extreme views about his work; unfortunately Newton's views on Greene, quite possibly unprintable, have not survived in the same way!

Greene's first book of his unique philosophical thoughts was published in 1712 under the splendid title *The Principles of Natural Philosophy, in which is shown the insufficiency of the present systems to give us any just account of that science* and was the subject of much contemporary ridicule and parody. Greene was not at all perturbed by this attack on his scholarship and continued to devote his life to the pursuit of knowledge, publishing a further massive work in 1727. This stretched to 980 pages and carried the even more elaborate title *The Principles of the Philosophy of the Expansive and Contractive Forces, or an Enquiry into the Principles of the Modern Philosophy, that is, into the several chief Rational Sciences which are extant.* This book was no better received than the first, and simply served to confirm what his colleagues already suspected, that the only person who seemed to be interested in Greene's views was Greene himself. He even went so far as to suggest a 'Greenian' philosophy which combined his own ideas with others current at the time and in the process seemed to equate the significance of his views with those of both Galileo and Descartes.

But it is the elaborate terms of the subsequent benefaction within his will that scale the twin peaks of eccentricity and absurdity with an ease that is not only breathtaking but which also reinforces his contemporaries' opinion that he was, quite simply, deranged.

To begin with, there was to be a bookshelf erected in the college library to hold the collection of books and memorabilia collected by Greene over his long and studiously unsuccessful life and which he wished to donate to the college. He then directed that memorial stones were to be erected to him in four locations: Clare College Chapel, King's College Chapel, Great St Mary's – the university church in the city centre, and the north chancel of the parish church in his home town of Tamworth. To accompany each of the stones, he also left long and glowing descriptions of himself and his life for good measure!

But the most unusual direction in Greene's will required that his body should first be dissected and that all the fragments, except the bones, should be collected and buried in All Saints' Church, Cambridge, unless a new college chapel had been built before his death, in which case the remains should be buried there. As for the bones, they were to be displayed in the library next to the bookshelf containing his earthly goods. Once the college had complied with the prescribed terms, it would become entitled, if it so desired, to inherit Greene's house in Tamworth, £200 in stocks and more odd instructions on the use of interest earned, after certain of his relatives had passed away.

No doubt anticipating Clare's reluctance to comply with these peculiar requests, Greene further directed that if Clare refused the bequest, it should be offered in turn to St John's, Trinity and Jesus colleges and, if they too declined, it should go to Sidney Sussex. However, life has a habit of frustrating such complicated plans, and Greene was staying with relatives in Tamworth when he died in August 1730. Although there is an unsubstantiated record of his having been buried in Cambridge, it is most unlikely that a body would have been moved so far for burial in those days, particularly in the heat of summer, and it is more than probable that Greene's body, bones and all, was buried in Tamworth.

The college complied with none of Greene's wishes at the time and in fact hesitated for twelve years before finally accepting the bequest in 1742. Five years later, six scholarships were established from the bequest and two annual prizes instituted in Greene's name, one for piety and one for learning. The prizes were to consist of two silver plates or tankards, costing not more than £6, and the recipients were required not only to receive them on their knees from the master but also to deliver a Latin oration in the hall, one in praise of religion, Christian piety and virtue and the other on learning. Greene further directed that regularity of attendance at the college chapel should be considered in selecting the candidate for the cup for piety.

With Greene having been buried some years previously, and probably at a good distance from the college, Clare was now faced with the problem of displaying the bones in the library. Greene's family eventually gave permission for another, this time anonymous, skeleton to be substituted for his own, and in due course this went on display in the library, then over the chapel. In 1763, when the new chapel was built, the skeleton was moved with the library to new accommodation over the hall and, in 1818, it was moved again when that area was converted to student rooms. This time, however, its final resting place was not quite as visible as it had been until then, for the skeleton had now, at long last, entered its famous cupboard which was situated at the top of the staircase near the hall.

It is supposed to have stayed in the cupboard for many years and was officially deemed to have disappeared, no doubt to the great relief of the college authorities, following the fire which destroyed much of that part of the building in October 1890. Nevertheless, stories linger of the skeleton's gradual disappearance before the fire at the hands of younger members of the college, and it is said that some of the livelier students of the time had acquired the habit of raiding the cupboard for the purposes of taking a bone with them when they left the college, by way of a souvenir. It would thus not have taken many such students for the skeleton in this particular cupboard to have completely disappeared in a relatively short time, unlike its proverbial descendants which, if anything, seem to be somewhat more persistently troublesome and less quietly removed.

But at least Greene's memory remains intact at Clare, even if his substitute skeleton does not, for his prizes, the Greene Cups, are still awarded for learning and for good behaviour, itself substituted for piety in fairly modern times, no doubt because good behaviour is seen as a more realistic achievement for the majority of modern students. Fortunately for present day recipients and their audience, they are no longer required either to receive the prizes on their knees or to deliver the oration in Latin.

Emmanuel College

Emmanuel College – Emma to collegiate Cambridge – stands on the east side of St Andrew's Street, removed like Downing and others from the historic heart of the city centre. Its most prominent entrance overlooks restaurants and building society offices, bookshops and florists, and confronts the heavy traffic flowing towards it from the Lion Yard car park along Downing Street, in addition to contending with the cumbersome manoeuvrings of buses heading for the central bus station on its north-eastern edge. For all that, the site is surprisingly spacious despite being confined on three sides by busy thoroughfares, because the main buildings are concentrated to the west of the site.

A Brief History

Emmanuel, like both Sidney Sussex and Jesus colleges, is built on the site of an earlier religious institution, in this instance a Dominican priory. Sir Walter Mildmay, Chancellor of the Exchequer to Queen Elizabeth I, bought the land for £550 and founded the college in 1584 as a 'seed-plot of learned men' for the newly formed Protestant Church. Many of Emmanuel's early members, including John Harvard, were among the settlers in New England. Harvard was only thirty-one years of age when he died of consumption in 1638, having been in New England for just two years. Half his estate, about £750, and his library of 320 books were bequeathed for the founding of the famous college which now bears his name in Boston, Massachusetts. More recently, Emmanuel College has produced a varied collection of eminent judges, scientists, writers and satirists.

The original priory had been founded in the thirteenth century in the area of New Court at the north-west of the site. The priory was dissolved in 1538 and remained unused until Mildmay's purchase and the granting of a foundation charter by Elizabeth. Ralph Symons was the architect of the conversion works which created the college's first chapel, on a north-south axis from the former refectory. At the same time, the old Dominican priory

Looking across Emmanuel College's First Court to the chapel, designed by Sir Christopher Wren, and the long gallery over the arcade

church became the hall. The conversions were completed in 1589 and no further building works were undertaken until well into the seventeenth century.

Brick Building, containing three floors of residential chambers and a garret, was completed in 1634, and was followed in 1667 by the completion of the Brewhouse at the eastern corner of the college grounds. A new chapel, properly orientated and designed by Sir Christopher Wren, was consecrated in 1674.

There followed a century of gradual alterations which started with the construction of the Westmoreland Building, forming the south side of Front Court, continued with the restyling of the adjoining older buildings and culminated in the development of the new front to St Andrew's Street which caused the relocation of the college's main entrance to Emmanuel Street.

After the completion of the north side of New Court in 1825, it was over sixty years before the next major project, the Hostel, got under way on a site to the south of the Brewhouse. There are no surviving plans or engravings of the original two-storey structure, but having been substantially modified during the eighteenth century it was by now coming to the end of its useful life. For around a hundred years the northern part of the Brewhouse, known once as the Dwelling House and later as Emmanuel House, had been rented to outside tenants, possibly because its accommodation was no longer considered suitable for the college's own use.

But another reason for its apparent unpopularity might just have been the house's unofficial occupants, whose noisy, and mostly unseen, perambulations had disturbed the various tenants for many years before the building's eventual demolition in 1893. In any event, the new Emmanuel House was completed in 1894 on the same site and still bears down rather oppressively on Parker Street to the north, but, so far, without the dubious benefit of the Ghost of Emmanuel House.

Emma's Ghost

It was in the late 1860s, when the building was approaching its bicentenary, that the first signs of a ghostly presence began to trouble the occupants. The sole tenant of the time was a widow, a

Mrs Harris, who had taken over the lease in about 1867 and who stayed in the house until about 1875 with several of her children. Mrs Harris had a drawing-room on the first floor of the house, connected to the hall stairs by a passageway which was the scene of the strange events that follow.

Mrs Harris had not been living in the house for more than a year or two when she first became aware of peculiar noises in the passage outside the drawing-room. Heavy, stamping footsteps would approach and then pass the drawing-room door before descending the staircase into the hall below, where they promptly ceased. Mrs Harris seems to have heard the noises on several occasions, along with members of her household, but there was no visible manifestation to assist in identifying the cause.

On one occasion Mrs Dunn, a friend of Mrs Harris and a frequent visitor to the house, was sitting reading in the drawing-room on a warm summer afternoon. Mrs Dunn knew of the stories of the noisy footsteps but had never believed that they were true. She had left the door open to the passage and was well aware that the only other person in the house at the time was Mrs Harris, who she knew was busy writing in the dining-room downstairs, having sent all the servants out for the afternoon. In a letter written to the Society for Psychical Research's investigator, Mrs Eleanor Sidgwick of Newnham College, some fifteen years later in 1885, she recalled being deeply engrossed in her reading that afternoon when her attention was distracted by the sound of a 'peculiar, loud step coming down the passage'. Knowing that that part of the house was empty, she went to the open door and looked into the passage, just as the heavy footsteps passed by. She continued looking with more than a little trepidation as the footsteps proceeded downstairs, but saw no one. Recovering from her fright, she called down to Mrs Harris to ask if she had heard anything. Mrs Harris replied that indeed she had, but she was used to it.

Not every visitor to Emmanuel House was alerted in advance to the existence of the ghost, and it fell to one such guest to provide the first visual impression of the apparition. Mrs Harris's young daughter-in-law, Emily, had been deliberately kept in ignorance of the story before coming to stay at Emmanuel House in about 1870.

She, too, wrote of her experiences in 1885, in a letter to Mrs Dunn, who was at the time collecting statements from various witnesses to pass on to Mrs Sidgwick.

It seems that Emily had been in bed a while one evening, with the lamp in the street outside casting a pale light into the room. Something made her suddenly look towards the dressing-table and sure enough there was, she thought, a short figure standing at its right-hand side. The apparition resembled a figure with a bridal veil thrown over it, although the veil looked more grey than white in the dull light from the street lamp. Emily believed at first that it was a reflection but soon realised that the figure was not going anywhere and began to feel both 'creepy and crawly'. She quickly sat up in bed and gazed at the ghost, which appeared completely unmoved by this show of defiance, before she retreated beneath the bedclothes, fearful that the ghost might drag the covers off her so that it could look upon her. Having stayed under the covers almost to the point of suffocation, Emily tentatively re-emerged to find that the ghost had disappeared.

Another member of the household, this time a young pageboy who had only been in Mrs Harris's employ for a few days, had no prior knowledge of the Emmanuel House Ghost before it appeared in his bedroom one night. Mrs Harris had even gone to the trouble of impressing upon the other servants the need to keep the young man in ignorance, but these instructions did not, naturally, extend to the ghost.

The boy woke one night to find the ghost in his room. His screams woke one of Mrs Harris's sons who, with the assistance of some medicinal brandy, was able to restore the boy to some degree of calmness. Unfortunately, the boy later had a fit, became more unwell and was sent from the house for good the following day. There is, of course, no surviving statement from him to clarify what he saw or where he saw it, except that it appears unlikely that he would have been occupying the same room in which Emily Harris had seen her veiled lady.

The Harris family left in about 1875, and after a few short tenancies Emmanuel House was let to Miss C.M. Bowen, who, unusually for college premises, opened a girls' school there in about

1881. Miss Bowen was the sister of Mrs Dunn, who herself was a good friend of Mrs Harris and who, it will be remembered, had heard but not seen the ghost passing the drawing-room many years previously.

Two years passed before Miss Bowen first became aware of the Emmanuel House Ghost. She had been sitting writing one evening in the dining-room, which was off the main entrance hall on the ground floor, and therefore not far away from the stairs, when she heard someone coming down the stairs. When the someone did not come into the dining-room to see her as she had expected, she went into the hall to look for them but saw nobody. Thinking it no more than odd, and not, by all accounts, being given to believing in ghosts, she returned to her writing and thought nothing more about it; until the same thing happened a little while later.

This time, she clearly heard the footsteps coming down the stairs and, thinking that it was a colleague that she wished to see, Miss Palmer, she called out to her as she opened the door into the hall. She was astonished to find, once more, that there was no one there. Mrs Dunn was less inclined to let the matter rest this time and proceeded to ask everyone in the house if they had come downstairs. Nobody had, but a servant, Miss Skippon, had also apparently heard the footsteps.

On two further occasions Miss Skippon, who was described at the time as 'middle-aged, sensible and decidedly unimaginative', heard a voice distinctly call 'Kate' from the general direction of the attic stairs when she was in her bedroom. Miss Skippon, whose Christian name was Kate, thought Miss Bowen was calling her, even though it was not like her voice, but saw nothing when she looked out of her room. Miss Bowen, who apparently believed that ghosts did not make sounds like these, remained puzzled by the events and thought that it was altogether most uncanny.

Although she had no further contact with the ghost, Miss Bowen would probably have been aware of another sighting a year or so later in 1884 by one of her teachers, Miss M. Bellamy. Miss Bellamy was described by Mrs Dunn as a strong-minded individual, a typical board school mistress, and had also been deliberately kept in ignorance of the many stories that Emmanuel

House was now accumulating, as no doubt all new members of staff were for obvious reasons.

She later wrote to Mrs Sidgwick that she had been standing in the kitchen, looking towards the garden door, when she saw what appeared to her to be a lady, a stranger, coming down the stairs. The lady crossed the hall and turned in the direction of the dining-room door. Miss Bellamy's attention was particularly drawn to the lady not only by her smooth, gliding movement, but also because her steps were perfectly noiseless even when she was only a few yards away. Miss Bellamy admitted later to an uncanny feeling being communicated to her at this point and she did not see or hear whether or not the dining-room door was opened and closed to allow the strange lady to pass. After a minute or so she went into the dining-room but there was no one to be seen. There was no other door into the room and, having made enquiries around the house, she could not find anybody in Emmanuel House at that particular time who had either been coming downstairs or been in the dining-room.

Miss Bowen and her school left Emmanuel House in the summer of 1885 after only four years of occupancy and for reasons which have not survived the years as well as the stories of its ghostly visitors. The new residents, Mr W.N. (later Sir William Napier) Shaw and his wife, were left alone by Mrs Sidgwick, who was in the middle of her investigations at the time, in case any future testimony of theirs might be prejudiced by prior knowledge of the strange footsteps and gliding figures reported by others. However, the Shaws had moved into the house after it had been done up to an extent, and that alone may have seen off the ghost once and for all.

Unfortunately, Mrs Sidgwick did not find enough in the way of evidence to justify publication in the *Journal of the Society for Psychical Research*, primarily because such information as she had collected was essentially second-hand, as Mrs Harris had recently died. Mrs Dunn, whom Mrs Sidgwick regarded as not only sensible and sober, but also excitable, imaginative and nervous, co-operated as well as she could, but without more eyewitnesses to question the investigations came to an end.

For all the inconclusiveness of the SPR's research, the Emmanuel House Ghost remains fascinating because of the way in which the accumulating stories were, in most cases, deliberately withheld from occupants new to the house. What they saw was not, so far as can be told at this distance, the subject of any preconceived notion, or of any scare-mongering on the part of the staff, but simply what they thought it was – a veiled lady on three occasions and a series of mysteriously loud footsteps moving along a passage and down the stairs on a number of others.

What unfortunate set of circumstances caused these events remains a mystery. Mrs Dunn was convinced that there had been three suicides in the house but had no further details to offer as to when they might have occurred, and the college's history of Emmanuel House reveals no clues as to the identities of those who might have initiated them. All we know with any certainty is that the old Emmanuel House was demolished in 1893 and that the new building of the same name that replaced it the following year has not yet revealed the successors to its earlier, unwelcome and often noisy visitors.

Jesus College

Jesus College has developed on one of the most spacious sites in the centre of the city, to the north of Jesus Lane and west of Victoria Avenue. Bounded to the north and east by one of Cambridge's many large open spaces, Jesus Green, the college buildings are surrounded by private gardens and playing-fields, unmatched in most of the other medieval foundations in the city. The main pedestrian approach to the college from Jesus Lane is through the long, high-walled passageway known as The Chimney, which also serves to separate the Master's and Fellows' gardens. It is unusual in the older colleges for the entrance building to be so remote from the nearest highway, and this is a consequence of the college's early history.

A Brief History

The 'College of the Blessed Mary the Virgin, St John the Evangelist, and the glorious Virgin St Radegund, near Cambridge', to give Jesus its full name, was founded in 1496 by the twenty-eighth Bishop of Ely, John Alcock, and occupies the oldest college buildings in Cambridge, even though it is by no means the oldest college. There had been a Benedictine nunnery on the site since its foundation outside the then city boundary in 1133 by an earlier bishop, but by the time of Alcock's visit there were only two nuns resident, and he was able to get Henry VII's permission to take over the buildings for the purposes of establishing a college.

The alterations started immediately, and by 1497 Henry had granted the foundation charter. The original buildings that were retained were the Nuns' Church, part of which became the college chapel, and Cloister Court which, with the remainder of the foreshortened church nave, formed the basis for the Master's Lodge and student accommodation. These early alterations obviously served the college well because, with the exception of the small south range of First Court built in the early sixteenth century, little new work was undertaken until the middle of the seventeenth century, when the north range of First Court was completed in 1642.

Walls had been erected around the Fellows' Garden (1608–9) and

The entrance gatehouse to Jesus College, looking north from Jesus Lane along the long, walled footpath called The Chimney

the Master's Garden (1681–2), forming The Chimney, there was some tinkering with the entrance gateway from Jesus Lane in the early eighteenth century, and in 1720 the south range of First Court was heightened. It was over a hundred years before the next sizeable extension, the east range of Second Court, finished in 1822, and over forty more before William Morris added to Pugin's earlier restoration work in the chapel. The north range of Second Court was built by Alfred Waterhouse in 1870 and was followed by the east range of Chapel Court in the 1880s.

Little more was started until after the First World War, when the enclosure of both Second Court and Chapel Court was effectively completed in 1923 and 1931 respectively. The main addition of the later twentieth century has been North Court but it is from the post-First World War period that the stories of Jesus ghosts first appeared in a collection of tales put together by Arthur Gray, Master of Jesus between 1912 and his death in 1940.

Arthur Gray was the last Master of Jesus to be elected for life – he was sixty at the time – and he also had the distinction of being the first layman to hold the post. In December 1919 Gray, using the pseudonym 'Ingulphus', published a book entitled *Tedious Brief Tales of Granta and Gramarye*, which was an anthology of ghostly stories first published in a number of local magazines. The characters named in the stories were all former, and deceased, members of the college and could thus be tracked down in college records, lending some degree of credibility to the tales themselves, as did the authenticity of the settings. Charles Bellasis, for example, was indeed a member of Jesus, but he went down more than a hundred years before the period in which this tale is set.

'The Everlasting Club', reproduced here in full, is set in a room of the college used at that time as a lumber room and which had been known as the Ghost Room for many, many years. Some five years after the story appeared, the room was returned to human occupation and has remained such ever since.

The Everlasting Club *by Arthur Gray*

There is a chamber in Jesus College the existence of which is probably known to few who are now resident, and fewer still have penetrated into it or even seen its interior. It is on the right hand of the landing on the top floor of the precipitous staircase in the angle of the cloister next the Hall – a staircase which for some forgotten story connected with it is traditionally called 'Cow Lane'. The padlock which secures its massive oaken door is very rarely unfastened, for the room is bare and unfurnished. Once it served as a place of deposit for superfluous kitchen ware, but even that ignominious use has passed from it, and it is now left to undisturbed solitude and darkness. For I should say that it is entirely cut off from the light of the outer day by the walling up, some time in the eighteenth century, of its single window, and such light as ever reaches it comes from the door, when rare occasion causes it to be opened.

The oaken door to the Ghost Room in 'Cow Lane'

Yet at no extraordinarily remote day this chamber has evidently been tenanted, and, before it was given up to darkness, was comfortably fitted, according to the standard of comfort which was known in college in the days of George II. There is still a roomy fireplace before which legs have been stretched and wine and gossip have circulated in the days of wigs and brocade. For the room is spacious and, when it was lighted by the window looking eastward over the fields and common, it must have been a cheerful place for a sociable don.

Let me state in brief, prosaic outline the circumstances

which account for the gloom and solitude in which this room has remained now for nearly a century and a half.

In the second quarter of the eighteenth century the University possessed a great number of clubs of a social kind. There were clubs in college parlours and clubs in private rooms, or in inns and coffee-houses: clubs flavoured with politics, clubs clerical, clubs purporting to be learned and literary. Whatever their professed particularity, the aim of each was convivial. Some of them, which included undergraduates as well as seniors, were dissipated enough, and in their limited provincial way aped the profligacy of such clubs as the Hell Fire Club of London notoriety.

Among these last was one which was at once more select and of more evil fame than any of its fellows. By a singular accident, presently to be explained, the Minute Book of this Club, including the years from 1738 to 1766, came into the hands of a Master of Jesus College, and though, so far as I am aware, it is no longer extant, I have before me a transcript of it which, though it is in a recent handwriting, presents in a bald shape such a singular array of facts that I must ask you to accept them as veracious. The original book is described as a stout duodecimo volume bound in red leather and fastened with red silken strings. The writing in it occupied some 40 pages, and ended with the date November 2, 1766.

The Club in question was called the Everlasting Club – a name sufficiently explained by its rules, set forth in the pocket-book. Its number was limited to seven, and it would seem that its members were all young men, between 22 and 30. One of them was a Fellow-Commoner of Trinity: three of them were Fellows of Colleges, among whom I should specially mention a Fellow of Jesus, named Charles Bellasis: another was a landed proprietor in the county, and the sixth was a young Cambridge physician. The Founder and President of the Club was the Honourable Alan Dermot, who, as the son of an Irish peer, had obtained a nobleman's degree in the University, and lived in idleness in the town. Very little is known of his life and character, but that little is highly in his disfavour.

He was killed in a duel in Paris in 1743, under circumstances which I need not particularise, but which point to an exceptional degree of cruelty and wickedness in the slain man.

I will quote from the first pages of the Minute Book some of the laws of the Club, which will explain its constitution:

'1. This Society consisteth of seven Everlastings, who may be Corporeal or Incorporeal, as Destiny shall determine.

2. The rules of the Society, as herein written, are immutable and Everlasting.

3. None shall hereafter be chosen into the Society and none shall cease to be its members.

4. The Honourable Alan Dermot is the Everlasting President of the Society.

5. The Senior Corporeal Everlasting, not being the President, shall be the Secretary of the Society, and in this Book of Minutes shall record its transactions, the date at which any Everlasting shall cease to be Corporeal, and all fines due to the Society . And when such Senior Everlasting shall cease to be Corporeal he shall, either in person or by some sure hand, deliver this Book of Minutes to him who shall be next Senior and at the time Corporeal, and he shall in like manner record the transactions therein and transmit it to the next Senior. The neglect of these provisions shall be visited by the President by fine or punishment according to his discretion.

6. On the second day of November in every year, being the Feast of All Souls, at ten o'clock post meridiem, the Everlastings shall meet at supper in the place of residence of that Corporeal member of the Society to whom it shall fall in order of rotation to entertain them, and they shall all subscribe in this Book of Minutes their names and present place of abode.

7. It shall be the obligation of every Everlasting to be present at the yearly entertainment of the Society, and none shall allege for excuse that he has not been invite thereto. If any Everlasting shall fail to attend the yearly meeting, or in his turn shall fail to provide entertainment for the Society, he shall be mulcted at the discretion of the President.

8. Nevertheless, if in any year, in the month of October and not less than seven days before the Feast of All Souls, the major part of the Society, that is to say, four at the least, shall meet and record in writing in these Minutes that it is their desire that no entertainment be given in that year, then, notwithstanding the two rules last rehearsed, there shall be no entertainment in that year, and no Everlasting shall be mulcted on the ground of his absence.'

The rest of the rules are either too profane or too puerile to be quoted here. They indicate the extraordinary levity with which the members entered upon their preposterous obligations. In particular, to the omission of any regulation as to the transmission of the Minute Book after the last Everlasting ceased to be 'Corporeal', we owe the accident that it fell into the hands of one who was not a member of the society, and the consequent preservation of its contents to the present day.

Low as was the standard of morals in all classes of the University in the first half of the eighteenth century, the flagrant defiance of public decorum by the members of the Everlasting Society brought upon it the strong censure of the authorities, and after a few years it was practically dissolved and its members banished from the University. Charles Bellasis, for instance, was obliged to leave the college, and, though he retained his fellowship, he remained absent from it for nearly twenty years. But the minutes of the society reveal a more terrible reason for its virtual extinction.

Between the years 1738 and 1743 the minutes record many meetings of the Club, for it met on other occasions besides that of All Souls Day. Apart from a great deal of impious jocularity on the part of the writers, they are limited to the formal record of the attendance of the members, fines inflicted, and so forth. The meeting on November 2nd in the latter year is the first about which there is any departure from the stereotyped forms. The supper was given in the house of the physician. One member, Henry Davenport, the former Fellow-Commoner of Trinity, was absent from the entertainment, as he was then serving in Germany, in the Dettingen campaign. The minutes contain an entry, 'Mulctatus propter absentiam per Presidentem, Hen. Davenport.' [Penalised for absence by the President, Hen. Davenport.] An entry on the next page of the book runs, 'Henry Davenport by a Cannon-shot became an Incorporeal Member, November 3, 1743.'

The minutes give in their own handwriting, under date November 2, the names and addresses of six other members. First in the list, in a large bold hand, is the autograph of 'Alan Dermot, President, at the Court of his Royal Highness.' Now in October Dermot had certainly been in attendance on the Young Pretender at Paris, and doubtless the address which he gave was understood at the time by the other Everlastings to refer to the fact. But on October 28, five days before the meeting of the Club, he was killed, as I have already mentioned, in a duel. The news of his death cannot have reached Cambridge on November 2, for the Secretary's record of it is placed below that of Davenport, and with the date November 10: 'this day was reported that the President was become an Incorporeal by the hands of a french chevalier.' And in a sudden ebullition, which is in glaring contrast with his previous profanities, he has dashed down 'The Good God shield us from ill.'

The tidings of the President's death scattered the Everlastings like a thunderbolt. They left Cambridge and buried themselves in widely parted regions. But the Club did not cease to exist. The Secretary was still bound to his hateful records: the five survivors did not dare to neglect their fatal obligations. Horror of the presence of the President made the November gathering once and forever impossible: but horror, too, forbade them to neglect the precaution of meeting in October of every year to put in writing their objection to the celebration. For five years five names are appended to that entry in the minutes, and that is all the business of the Club. Then another member died, who was not the Secretary.

For eighteen more years four miserable men met once each year to deliver the same formal protest. During those years we gather from the signatures that Charles Bellasis returned to Cambridge, now, to appearance, chastened and decorous. He occupied the rooms which I have described on the staircase in the corner of the cloister.

Then in 1766 comes a new handwriting and an altered minute: 'Jan. 27, on this day Francis Witherington, Secretary, became an Incorporeal Member. The same day this Book was delivered to me, James Harvey.' Harvey lived only a month, and a similar entry on March 7 states that the book has descended, with the same mysterious celerity to William Catherston. Then, on May 18, Charles Bellasis writes that on that day, being the date of Catherston's decease, the Minute Book has come to him as the last surviving Corporeal of the Club.

As it is my purpose to record fact only I shall not attempt to describe the feelings of the unhappy Secretary when he penned that fatal record. When Witherington died it must have come home to the three survivors that after twenty-three years' intermission the ghastly entertainment must be annually renewed, with the addition of fresh incorporeal guests, or that they must undergo the pitiless censure of the President. I think it likely that the terror of the alternative, coupled with the mysterious delivery of the Minute Book, was answerable for the speedy decease of the first two successors to the Secretaryship. Now that the alternative was offered to Bellasis alone, he was firmly resolved to bear the consequences, whatever they might be, of any infringement of the Club rules.

The graceless days of George II had passed away from the University. They were succeeded by times of outward respectability, when religion and morals were no longer publicly challenged. With Bellasis, too, the petulance of youth had passed: he was discreet, perhaps exemplary. The scandal of his early conduct was unknown to most of the new generation, condoned by the few survivors who had witnessed it.

On the night of November 2nd, 1766, a terrible event revived in the older inhabitants of the College the memory of those evil days. From ten o'clock to midnight a hideous uproar went on in the chamber of Bellasis. Who were his companions none knew. Blasphemous outcries and ribald songs, such as had not been heard for twenty years past, aroused from sleep or study the occupants of the court; but among the voices was not that of Bellasis. At twelve a sudden silence fell upon the cloisters. But the Master lay awake all night, troubled at the relapse of a respected colleague and the horrible example of libertinism set to his pupils.

In the morning all remained quiet about Bellasis' chamber. When his door was opened, soon after daybreak, the early light creeping through the drawn curtains revealed a strange scene. About the table were drawn seven chairs, but some of them had been overthrown, and the furniture was in chaotic disorder, as after some wild orgy. In the chair at the foot of the table sat the lifeless figure of the Secretary, his head bent over his folded arms, as though he would shield his eyes from some horrible sight. Before him on the table lay pen, ink and the red Minute Book. On the last inscribed page, under the date of November 2nd, were written, for the first time since 1742, the autographs of the seven members of the Everlasting Club, but without address. In the same strong hand in which the President's name was written there was appended below the signatures the note, 'Mulctatus per Presidentum propter neglectum obsonii, Car. Bellasis.' [Penalised by the President for neglecting the victuals, Charles Bellasis.]

The Minute Book was secured by the Master of the College, and I believe that he alone was acquainted with the nature of its contents. The scandal reflected on the College by the circumstances revealed in it caused him to keep the knowledge rigidly to himself. But some suspicion of the nature of the occurrences must have percolated to students and servants, for there was a long-abiding belief in the College that annually on the night of November 2 sounds of unholy revelry were heard to issue from the chamber of Bellasis. I cannot learn that the occupants of the adjoining rooms have ever been disturbed by them. Indeed, it is plain from the minutes that owing to their improvident drafting no provision was made for the perpetuation of the All Souls entertainment after the last Everlasting ceased to be Corporeal. Such superstitious belief must be treated with contemptuous incredulity. But whether for that cause or another the rooms were shut up, and have remained tenantless from that day to this.

Thus ends Arthur Gray's imaginative tale, and there is little to add by way of a postscript, except to remind the reader that the room formerly known as the Ghost Room, situated at the top of 'G' Staircase, ceased to be a lumber room in 1924 and has been 'corporeally' occupied ever since. Sadly, there are no further reports of mysterious goings-on, but, bearing in mind the fate that befell Bellasis and his fellow Everlastings, incorporeal or otherwise, perhaps it is just as well.

Arthur Gray, Master of Jesus from 1912 to 1940, published an anthology of the college's ghost stories. (Painting by Sir William Nicholson.)

Renamed St Mary the Less or Little St Mary's, this church was formerly St Peter-without-Trumpington-Gate, from which Peterhouse got its name

Peterhouse

Peterhouse is located mostly on the west side of Trumpington Street, north of the Fitzwilliam Museum, and to the east of the small stretch of Coe Fen adjacent to the river, where one of Cambridge's better hotels is situated. To the north is the Church of St Mary the Less, more commonly known as Little St Mary's which, under a different name, had much to do with Peterhouse in its early days.

Trumpington Street, with its potentially dangerous open gutters down both sides, leads south to one of the main exit routes from the city towards London as it has done for centuries, and the college's east-facing frontage is dominated by the college chapel set symmetrically between the library and the Burroughs Building, behind the classically detailed cast-iron railings.

Across the street from the chapel is the elegantly Georgian Master's Lodge bequeathed to the college in 1726 and, to its rear, Cosin Court, the newest building on the site.

A Brief History

Peterhouse is the oldest college in Cambridge and the smallest, with just over 200 undergraduates. Its early history is inextricably bound up with that of the university in Cambridge and has been described in detail earlier in this book.

The second half of the thirteenth century in Cambridge was characterised by the growing number of increasingly unruly students with no settled accommodation. The problem was not confined to Cambridge, and although the collegiate system of providing accommodation dedicated to students originated in Paris it was from Merton College in Oxford, founded in 1264, that Hugh de Balsham, Bishop of Ely, took the idea and founded a small college in Cambridge in 1280.

In 1284 the college moved to better premises on its present site next to the Church of St Peter-without-Trumpington-Gate. In 1286 de Balsham died and bequeathed money sufficient to buy land and build the hall which, albeit much altered, still forms an integral part of the south range of Old Court. The students and fellows, with no chapel of their own, worshipped in St Peter's, and when the church was rebuilt and renamed St Mary the Less in 1340 the connection was retained in the college's name at the time, St Peter's College.

The library was added at the end of the sixteenth century and, in 1628, the two original hostels on the site were demolished to make way for the new chapel. The master of the time was Dr Matthew Wren whose better known nephew, Christopher, completed his first building, the chapel at Pembroke College, almost opposite Peterhouse, in 1665. Soon after its completion the chapel at Peterhouse was badly damaged by Parliamentarian soldiers, and the main windows were not properly repaired until 1855.

The next major addition was a block of chambers designed by Sir James Burroughs and finished in 1742, and it was a further eighty years or so before another accommodation block, Gisborne Court, was built, but the major work of the nineteenth century was George Gilbert Scott's restoration of the hall in 1870. At the same time, William Morris and the pre-Raphaelites, Burne-Jones, Ford Madox Brown and Philip Webb, all contributed to the interior with striking stained glass windows and decorative tiling. Further student

Peterhouse chapel

housing has been added during this century, most notably Fen Court of 1939 and the William Stone Building of 1964.

Peterhouse's past students include Thomas Gray the poet, Charles Babbage, inventor of the 'difference engine', generally regarded as the first computer, and two aeronautical pioneers, Sir Frank Whittle, who invented the jet engine, and Sir Christopher Cockerel, inventor of the hovercraft.

The Election That Went Wrong

The eighteenth century was a period of considerable turbulence within the university and its constituent societies and colleges, with numerous scandals and misused patronage. Peterhouse was no exception to this and, while the story presented here does not involve a ghost in the traditional sense, the intrigue which contributed to the death of Francis Dawes could certainly have sustained such a reminder of the misfortune that befell both him and, to a lesser extent, the college.

The story begins on 17 August 1787 with the death of the Master of Peterhouse, Edmund Law, Bishop of Carlisle. Law, who had a BA from St John's and an MA from Christ's College, had been appointed Master in 1754 and, in accordance with a custom that existed into the twentieth century, would hold that position until his death, irrespective of the state of his physical and mental health.

At the time, Peterhouse was one of four colleges within the university to have the Bishop of Ely, Dr James Yorke, as its Visitor. The Visitor's role was important, all the more so in this case because Yorke's predecessor was the college's founder. In essence, his responsibility was to supervise the conduct of college business and to interfere when invited by the fellows or when he considered it necessary, but in most instances the colleges were models of propriety in managing their own affairs, so interference was rare.

The procedures to be used in appointing a new master were laid down in the statutes presented to the college by Simon de Montacute in 1338 and had evolved to a point where, unlike many of their contemporaries elsewhere in Cambridge, the Fellows of Peterhouse had the opportunity to contribute to the selection process not only by nominating two candidates for presentation to the Bishop, who would then make the final decision, but also by indicating which of the two was their preference. The other requirements for the candidates were that they should both be bachelors of divinity and that one should have been born in the south of England and one in the north.

The college's Senior Fellow, Francis Dawes, who also acted as bursar for many years, immediately began making the necessary arrangements for the election of a new master. Dawes had spent all his adult life at Peterhouse. He was admitted in 1750, obtained a fellowship in 1758 and became one of the two Esquire Bedells of the university in 1755. This was originally an executive post which involved attendance on the Chancellor and Vice-Chancellor at public ceremonies and which still exists as an entirely ceremonial role. Dawes thus arranged for the election of the two candidates to be presented to the Bishop to take place in the college chapel on 31 August.

It had long been appreciated within college circles that there were two natural candidates with the appropriate academic qualifications, and yearning, for the position of master. There was no suitable candidate from the north of England among the fellows, and so Daniel Longmire, a vicar and former Fellow born in the north who had retained his membership of the college for many years, and George Borlase, a younger Fellow and tutor born in the south, became the acknowledged candidates for nomination.

As election day approached, it became clear that Borlase had the majority of fellows on his side, and in more normal circumstances that would probably have been that. But Longmire had been of considerable assistance to the Bishop's older brother, Lord Hardwicke, some time before and thus felt confident of the Bishop's support, as well as that of his colleagues, in securing the nomination. Borlase also reasoned that Longmire, a former Fellow, would certainly become master if he was nominated as one of the two candidates, and Borlase therefore decided to exploit the college's statute that required the candidates to be fellows, feeling sure that the others would be more inclined to disregard Longmire if there was another current and suitably qualified Fellow standing.

Borlase and his followers began courting the chosen stalking-horse, Frances Barnes, a Fellow and Vice-Provost of King's College.

Barnes was assured that he stood no chance of being elected Master of Peterhouse, because the Bishop would be certain to select Borlase; his only role would be to deprive the Bishop of an opportunity to appoint Longmire. Borlase kept his plan from both Longmire and Francis Dawes until the morning of the election when both were informed of the late entrance of a further candidate.

The election proceeded later that morning with eleven of the fourteen fellows then present in the college casting their votes, after the appropriate statutes had been read to them in the comparatively modest surroundings of the college chapel. Borlase received eleven votes, Barnes eight and Longmire three (one of which was probably from Dawes), and Borlase must have felt that everything was moving as he had hoped. Three days later two fellows arrived at the Bishop's Gloucestershire home, complete with all the necessary documents and the nominees themselves, and made the Bishop aware of the college's preference for Borlase. But Bishop Yorke was not to be hurried. He had known nothing of the election, he was not going to be forced to a decision for the convenience of others and, more to the point, he smelt a rat, in the form of a nominee who, although a Fellow and a bachelor of divinity, was not a Fellow of Peterhouse. The fellows were dismissed and returned to Cambridge without a decision.

Longmire and Dawes travelled to Gloucestershire to meet the Bishop on 8 September, and Longmire staked his claim for preference over Barnes because, although not then a Fellow, he was at least a member of the college. The Bishop sought legal opinion and, on arriving in London a fortnight later, was advised that the actions of the fellows had been contrary to the statutes and that he, as Visitor of the college, had the right to select a new master without consulting the fellows. This he did in a letter to the college on 28 September.

The Bishop's letter, vetted by his legal adviser, Dr Harris, stated the grounds upon which he was taking the appointment of the new master into his own hands and then declared the result of the election null and void. He concluded by appointing Daniel Longmire as master and thereby started a protracted legal battle that would do few people any good.

On 3 October a majority of the fellows then resident replied to Bishop Yorke, maintaining that the election was in accordance with the statutes, and at the same time lodged a formal protest at the college. Barnes, too, protested to the Bishop. Another Fellow, a lawyer named Edward Law, who had not been party to the earlier proceedings, came forward to support the majority. The Bishop was asked to suspend his nomination until Edward Law had spoken to him but declined, again on questionable legal advice, and to his later regret, and on 9 October Yorke issued an episcopal mandate formally appointing Longmire to the mastership.

Francis Dawes now had the unenviable job of reading the mandate to the fellows and called a college meeting on 15 October for that purpose. Four other fellows in residence attended, including Borlase, and resolved by a majority to apply to the courts for a writ, a mandamus, that would compel the Bishop to appoint either Barnes or Borlase to the mastership, but this did not prevent Longmire's formal induction ceremony from proceeding. In the event, only Dawes accompanied Longmire into the hall for the taking of oaths and the making of the formal declaration because, irrespective of his opinions and feelings, his position as Senior Fellow demanded it.

The fellows duly applied to the King's Bench for the writ early in the Michaelmas term, and it was not long before the Bishop's resolve, along with that of Dr Harris, was seen to waver because Longmire offered to resign his living in Linton, south of Cambridge, in favour of Borlase, provided that Longmire remain master. Borlase refused. In the ensuing months detailed arguments were put to the King's Bench, mostly to do with the interpretation of the medieval Latin text in which the statutes were cast, and on 14 April 1788 the court granted the mandamus that the college had requested.

Bishop Yorke had lost as much because of bad legal advice as by acting beyond the limits of his authority, and it was now up to him, as Visitor, to act in a way that would rise above the unpleasantness of the preceding months for the good of the college as a whole. Unfortunately for all concerned he did not.

On 2 May Borlase and Barnes were summoned to the Bishop's London residence. He knew the college preferred Borlase and he

Peterhouse chapel vestibule, where Francis Dawes hanged himself in the bell-ropes

knew that Barnes had been involved by others simply to frustrate the prospects of his own likely favourite, Longmire. After a lengthy explanation of his motives and reasons for so doing, he nevertheless announced that he intended to appoint Barnes as the new Master of Peterhouse. Barnes, who had not wanted the position in the first place, immediately began to behave in an insulting and insolent manner, saying that he did not believe himself to be the proper choice and that such an appointment would throw the college into even greater confusion. The Bishop ignored his pleas and on 3 May issued his new mandate in favour of Barnes, making it clear as he did so that he did not choose to be laughed at or triumphed over by the college.

Borlase, undoubtedly upset by the Bishop's contrary act, tried all the same to calm things down and persuaded the Bishop to defer the effective date for the mandate to allow the college to submit another petition to him. The Bishop agreed but was unmoved when nine fellows signed the petition in favour of Borlase, so on 12 May 1788 Francis Barnes became the reluctant Master of Peterhouse.

As a consequence of these events, Longmire was removed from his mastership and offered, by way of compensation, the vicarage of Linton in addition to that of Newton. But his failing health had not been helped by this unsettling period, and he died on 10 November 1789, to be replaced as vicar of Newton by George Borlase.

Francis Dawes had on several occasions throughout the election process been placed in difficult situations by virtue of his position as Senior Fellow. Whether he agreed with them or not, he was obliged to carry out the Bishop's mandates, and his formal institution of Longmire, with only the two of them present, can hardly have been the pleasurable affair he might have expected it to be. He would certainly have become unpopular with the other fellows for not joining with them in standing up against the Bishop's unreasonable behaviour, and the court's decision in favour of the college must have embarrassed, if not hurt, him deeply.

On 28 September 1789, two years to the day after the Bishop's first letter appointing Longmire to the mastership, Francis Dawes hanged himself in the bell-ropes of the college chapel, where the three-way election had taken place. No message was left by him, and there was no apparent reason for his suicide. A contemporary report of his funeral on 2 October at the former college chapel, Little St Mary's, states that a prodigious crowd of spectators had assembled from all over Cambridge and neighbouring districts out of affection and respect for him, including the Vice-Chancellor, Dr Farmer, who was also Dawes' executor. In his will, proven shortly after the funeral, Dawes bequeathed £100 each to the college and Addenbrooke's Hospital.

If there was ever to be a spectre emanating from the events related in this story it is unlikely that it would have been that of Dawes. He was, after all, only doing the job his position required, however unpleasant it might have been for him and his colleagues at the time. The one character who acted meanly throughout the affair and whose malign influence was felt well beyond his death was James Yorke, Bishop of Ely and Visitor to Peterhouse. Yorke's overtly spiteful appointment of Barnes to the mastership, against both Barnes' wishes and that of the fellows, was to haunt the college well into the nineteenth century.

Barnes therefore, in accordance with contemporary custom, became master for life when he was appointed in May 1788 at the age of forty-five. He was still master when Victoria acceded to the throne in 1837 and died at the age of ninety-five on May Day in 1838, just two days short of the fiftieth anniversary of his appointment. Barnes had soon proved to be poorly qualified for the post he did not want, and his shortcomings quickly became all too apparent to the other members of the college on whom he had been forced. Despite his appointment as professor of moral philosophy in 1813, he seemed to display an inability to discharge well any duties which required moral judgement and decency, but despite his incompetence it was not Barnes that had suffered most in the end.

It was Peterhouse, its reputation and its scholars that suffered for the entire and considerable duration of his mastership. That was solely the result of the ill-considered risk Borlase and the other fellows took when, in what they thought was a clever tactical move, they selected Barnes as their stalking-horse knowing him to be both unwilling and unsuitable and, if they had been alive at the end of that half-century of disappointment and frustration, they would still have had nobody to blame but themselves.

St John's College

The Charter of the College of St John the Evangelist was granted on 9 April 1511, some two years after the death of its founder, Lady Margaret Beaufort, the daughter of Henry VII. Lady Margaret had already founded Christ's College as well as establishing a lectureship in divinity but was persuaded by Bishop Fisher to undertake a new foundation on the site of the thirteenth-century hospital of the Monks of St John.

There is a ghost story associated with St John's College, but neither the subject nor its haunts will be found in the college or indeed in the city and county of Cambridge, but in a small village near the new M40 motorway almost twenty miles due north of 'the other place', as Oxford is known to the academics of Cambridge. Nor is there any real connection with the other place except that some of the characters concerned had either studied or taught at both universities.

A Brief History

The village of Souldern in Oxfordshire is roughly halfway between Banbury and Bicester, and the rectory attached to the Church of St Mary the Virgin in the village had originally been under the control of the Church. However, at some point in the reign of Elizabeth I, the Crown had taken over the right to appoint the rector under a forfeiture. This right of patronage was much valued and was known as a 'living' because it amounted to the patron providing employment, and thus a living, for a clergyman as well as being able to derive income from any associated lands and no doubt influence in local affairs.

The living at Souldern had been granted to John Williams, once Bishop of Lincoln and later Archbishop of York and Keeper of the Great Seal, by James I and was bestowed by Williams to the college in 1622. The rector appointed in that year was a Mr Harding who occupied the post until 1645 and who is best remembered for having rebuilt the parsonage during his incumbency.

Williams was nothing if not generous to his former college,

Ornamentation on the Great Gate of St John's College

having at various times given more than £2,000 for the library, £160 for founding scholarships, many valuable books and parcels of land as well as three other livings. However, not all the benefactions worked out as the college had been led to believe they would. By 1651, the income being provided by the lands, which should have

Drawing of the now demolished Souldern Rectory, north of Oxford

been £55 per year, was amounting to no more than £40, despite careful management, and was sufficient only to maintain the scholars and not the fellows. Consequently, in reporting this to the Committee for the Reformation of the University, the college acknowledged that its Fellowship Fund was £500 in debt and was given leave to discontinue the fellowships.

But all was not well with the living at Souldern either, and the college was clearly anxious as a result because a rival title to the living had been acquired in 1653 by the then rector, Thomas Hodges. Hodges himself was a controversial figure for such an appointment in the first place for he was not a member of St John's, having studied at Emmanuel College. It appears that he had been 'intruded' into St John's College by the Earl of Manchester, with the approval of a body of churchmen called the Assembly of Divines. Hodges was duly presented by the college to Souldern in 1647 and, having acquired the rival title in 1653, held onto it for nine years before eventually conveying it to St John's in 1662 'in consideration of his great and true respect to piety and learning and particularly to St John's Colledge'. Hodges was replaced in the following year as rector, and it was over thirty-five years later in 1698 that Geoffrey Shaw took up the appointment to the living, although he did not take up residence in Souldern until the following year.

Shaw had been admitted to St John's in 1676 at the age of eighteen and after a succession of academic awards became a Fellow in 1680. Among his various official duties he was an examiner in mathematics and reader in geometry, two of the seven liberal arts that formed the university curriculum of the day. From 1687 until 1696 he was vicar of Hauxton with Newton, villages some five miles south of Cambridge, and could little have expected that he would in the fullness of time become one of the central characters in what is certainly one of the most curious of ghost stories.

The Story of the Story

The story itself first appeared in a pamphlet published in London a year after the extraordinary events that had taken place at the rectory in the summer and autumn of 1706. It has subsequently been reworked and rewritten a number of times, appearing in college histories and in a history of Souldern parish itself, and it thus goes without saying that discrepancies in more than a few of the details have crept into the tale and created much confusion in the process. Typical of these was a nineteenth-century error which confused the true identity of the apparition with that of a local Oxford cleric with an identical name and of similar age, but with no Cambridge connection whatsoever.

The Ghost of Souldern Rectory

The essence of the story has remained the same over the years and starts with a leisurely trip by Robert Grove, a Fellow of St John's and Registrary of the University, into the West Country at the end of the summer term in 1706. Grove, himself the son of a clergyman and educated at Eton, knew Shaw well and stayed with him briefly on his way further west, promising to stay with him again for a longer visit on his return journey. This he did in the first week of August, and it was during the course of this visit that Grove heard of the strange 'meeting' Shaw had experienced the previous week, around 28 July.

Late one evening, towards midnight, Shaw was sitting reading and smoking in the study of the rectory when there appeared in front of him the spectre of John Naylor, dressed in a gown and cassock and with his hands clasped in front of him, exactly as he had appeared in life at St John's College. Naylor was an old companion of Shaw's in college but had died in November 1701, almost five years before. Shaw, remembering Naylor well, was not a little surprised to see 'him', and the apparition, having been invited to sit down close to Shaw, then began its extraordinary conversation.

Bidding Shaw not to be afraid, Naylor started by saying that he was there to acquaint him with something that greatly concerned him. As the conversation continued between them, Naylor told Shaw that their mutual friend Arthur Orchard was to die suddenly, that Shaw himself would die soon after and that he had come to forewarn Shaw so that he might prepare himself accordingly. There is no surviving record of Shaw's immediate reaction to this devastating news but it appears that they talked in all for about two hours on a variety of topics.

Shaw asked if it might be possible to form some idea of the other world, based upon life in this one. Naylor said that there was not but did not elaborate further, beyond adding that he himself was well. Shaw, pursuing the point, inquired if there were any of his old acquaintances with him, and Naylor again said no, much to Shaw's surprise. As the conversation drew to a close, Shaw asked if Naylor would stay longer but Naylor said that he was allotted only three days' absence and he was at the end of that period, so he could not oblige his old friend. Shaw invited him to return for another conversation before his time came but again Naylor declined, saying that it could not be, at which point he disappeared. It is hardly surprising that, according to Grove's account, Shaw spent a long time that night pacing his study after the apparition's departure, thinking over the curious events of the evening.

Despite the assertion by the writer of one of the less 'tabloid' contemporary sources for this tale that Shaw was known not to believe in apparitions, and indeed often argued against them, he must have been worried about his experience to have shared it with a guest almost twenty years his junior.

Grove, who it will be remembered heard this story a week or so after its occurrence, took leave of Shaw and continued on his return journey to Cambridge, stopping off again within a day or two at the house of a curate he knew who was also a Fellow of St John's. The precise identity and location of his parish seem to have eluded the many investigators of this story over the years, but it may have been Caxton, a small village east of St Neots on the main road to Cambridge and thus well within range of interesting college gossip, for when Grove arrived, the curate, Peter Clark, had some remarkable news for him.

Grove, asking after college news, was shocked to hear that Arthur Orchard had died suddenly that same week at the age of forty-seven during the evening of 6 August, while his bedmaker was fetching his supper from the college kitchens. Grove returned to St John's a day before Orchard's funeral at All Saints' Church, from which only the churchyard survives today, just across from St John's College main entrance. Much of the early credibility of the story rests upon his not being at all surprised at hearing the news of Orchard's death on his return to Cambridge, even though it would not have been impossible for the news to have travelled the few miles to Caxton, if that was where he had stayed with Clark, in the day or two between the death and Grove's arrival there.

Within little more than three months of Orchard's death in a chair in his room at St John's, Geoffrey Shaw, rector of Souldern, died instantly as he fell from behind a reading-desk into the aisle of the church and fractured his skull on the stone floor. The date was Sunday, 17 November 1706, and Shaw had been reading the second lesson of the day, from I Timothy 6: 19: 'Laying up in store for themselves a good foundation against the time to come, that they may lay hold on eternal life.' The Bible from which Shaw was reading, an edition of 1660 with the text for the day marked, still survives in the Oxfordshire Archives. Shaw's funeral was held on 8 December, with the sermon being preached by William Offley, a rector from a neighbouring parish and a former student at King's College, Cambridge.

That the apparition's first prediction came true was unusual enough but the arrival in Cambridge of the news of this latest tragedy must have caused Grove and his colleagues great consternation because the story seems to have circulated rapidly. Grove told the story of Naylor's apparition to Shaw to a colleague, Edmund Waller, who had been appointed to a fellowship the year before and who was to become a medical Fellow two years later. Waller was an ardent letter-writer and wrote on 12 December, only four days after Shaw's funeral, to his friend Thomas Offley, brother of the William Offley who had read the funeral sermon.

Thomas Offley then wrote back to his brother on 18 December, adding his own comments as well as enclosing Waller's letter to him, and asked for further hard facts such as the date of Shaw's will and his state of mind at the time of his death. The story itself ended up being published in a variety of forms, mostly based upon Waller's letters, and aroused much interest, not only within the university but in the country at large, because there was a strong element of credibility about the basic facts.

The characters in the story were serious and studious men, some of them scientists not likely to be given to flights of fancy. Robert Grove, in particular, was known to be a sceptic like Shaw on such matters but was obviously sufficiently moved by the story of the strange meeting to tell at least three people, including a local Member of Parliament, about the spectre's sinister predictions well before Shaw's death. Waller, who probably did more than anyone to broadcast the story, was to become a medical Fellow and therefore can be assumed to be of a sensible disposition. Shaw himself must have been sure of what he had seen to have ventured to discuss it with Grove in the first place.

Nevertheless, for all Grove's conviction, those he told seem to have kept remarkably quiet about the predictions, at least until they had come true, and even Shaw, the percipient, made no changes to his will after the visitation. Unfortunately, the rectory building in which these strange events took place no longer exists. Within a hundred years or so of the two deaths so accurately foretold in Naylor's conversation with Shaw there are reports of the appointed incumbents having to pay considerable sums out of their own pockets to repair the structure, and by 1890 it had been demolished and with it the haunt of John Naylor.

Christ's College

Christ's is one of the most central of the colleges in the old city centre, filling a triangular site with the majority of its buildings at the southern apex. Its entrance, the Great Gate in St Andrew's Street, is close to the fork with Hobson Street which forms the college's western boundary and matches the splendour of those at Trinity and St John's to the north of the centre, but without their

The north façade of the Fellows' Building – from the Fellows' Garden

benefit of open space from which to admire its beauty. The approach is cluttered with the cycles and pedestrians, tourists and students that inevitably fill the narrow pavements so close to the heart of the shopping area. To the east is Christ's Pieces, the smallest of the wide, open spaces in the city and more like an urban park than the others, and to the north King Street, famous for the King Street Run, a legendary drinking-race, involving purposeful attendance at several public houses in a very short space of time.

A Brief History

Christ's College was originally established as a small college, God's House, by William Byngham, a London parish priest, in about 1437. Its aim was to encourage students to read for lesser degrees than those available elsewhere, so that they would be suitably trained to become teachers and thus replace the thousands that had fallen victim to the Black Death. The original site was near King's College Chapel, and when in 1446 Henry VI expressed a wish to expand his foundation at King's, God's House was obliged to vacate the site and move to its present location. A foundation charter was granted by Henry in 1448, and over the next half-century work progressed on First Court.

Within a few years, Bishop Fisher had persuaded Lady Margaret Beaufort to refound the college and when, on 1 May 1505, a new charter was granted by her son, Henry VII, the college was newly dedicated to Jesus Christ. Lady Margaret's bequest, it will be remembered, founded St John's, but at Christ's College she had had the opportunity to see the fruits of her generosity and some of the buildings in First Court, including the Great Gate, remain more or less as she would have known them.

The next building to be started was in complete contrast to the medieval style of First Court. The Fellows' Building, completed about 130 years after First Court in 1643, is one of the most original early classical buildings in Cambridge, if not in England, and should have been the beginnings of the enclosure of Second Court, but the design was for an essentially free-standing structure which proved difficult to extend, and it has stayed fully detached ever since, at the north side of the Court.

After a further hundred years or so, First Court was refaced in the classical fashion of the time, and in 1823 the south range of Second Court was completed. From 1875 a comparatively intense period of expansion took place. The rebuilt hall was completed in 1879, the north range of Third Court was built in 1888–9 in a similar style to the Fellows' Building, and the library was extended some nine years later.

The twentieth century saw further additions to the college accommodation, the most notable and notorious of which has been

Sir Denys Lasdun's New Court, which in providing its inhabitants with on-site parking and uninterrupted views over the college grounds to the south also managed, until recent improvements and additions, to provide King Street to the north with one of the bleakest building backsides anywhere.

Notable scholars at Christ's have included John Milton, who came up in 1628 – there is a mulberry-tree named in his memory in the Fellows' Garden, and Charles Darwin, who entered the college in 1825. Darwin left Christ's in 1831 to join HMS *Beagle* on its five-year voyage to South America and the Galapagos Islands, during which his observations led him to develop his theory of evolution, eventually publishing *On the Origin of Species by Means of Natural Selection* in 1859.

The Ghost of Christopher Round

The story of the apparition of Christopher Round was originally published in 1918 in a book entitled *A College Mystery*, written by a former lecturer in history, A.P. Baker. Baker was born in Algoa Bay, Cape Province, South Africa, in 1873 and came up to Christ's in 1892. A serious accident playing football crippled him for life, and he left the college in 1895, only returning to Cambridge in 1903. He died in 1919 at the age of forty-six.

It may have been Baker's special experience and knowledge as a historian, combined with the way in which it was presented, that has given the story more credibility than was perhaps intended at the time. The setting is certainly authentic, and the various buildings and places in and around the college, in which the story is set, still exist. Unfortunately, there is no record of the characters in *Dr Peile's Biographical Register of Christ's College 1505–1905*, a list of all the members of the college over that period. Neither do any of the other named characters, who were supposedly members of other colleges, feature in their respective admission books and registers, so it can only be concluded that the names are fictitious. The characters, the story and the apparition, of course, may not be.

Baker's story, mostly written in the first person, is some eighty pages long and cannot, unfortunately, be included in its entirety. What follows is thus an account of the events portrayed rather than an abridgement of the narrative itself. It begins with a preface by Baker, explaining the background of the stories of an apparition, independently told to him by various fellows. Baker then describes Simon Goodridge's papers which had come into his possession some time previously. These form the core of the story and consist of Christopher Round's Record, contemporary newspaper reports and Goodridge's own notes, with an introductory summary of the fellows' experiences of the apparition. According to a postscript contained in Goodridge's notes, 'most' of the statements made by Round in his record are true, but since Round blocked its publication for fifty years after his death in the late 1860s, there was naturally little opportunity for Baker to check the facts.

The College Mystery

The four fellows consulted by Baker all had the same broad recollection of the apparition, each having seen it many times. The sightings were generally on moonlit summer nights and always in the Fellows' Garden. The figure of a tall, heavy, elderly man, dressed in black and wearing an old-fashioned swallow-tailed coat and beaver hat would emerge from the shadows of a group of large chestnut-trees and walk, slowly, deliberately and with head bowed across the lawns, following the same circuitous path and stopping at the same yew-tree each time, before disappearing into more shadows. So clear was the figure in the moonlight that none of the fellows thought that it was anything other than one of their colleagues out for a walk before retiring.

Only one of the fellows had more to tell. He remembered that on one occasion, a few minutes after seeing the figure in the garden, he had heard slow, heavy footsteps mounting the staircase shared by his room and that which was once occupied by Christopher Round, followed by the sound of the opening and closing of the door to that room.

The Record of Christopher Round

Round was born in Derbyshire at the beginning of the nineteenth century, the son of a village rector. When he wrote his Record at the age of seventy, his only surviving relative was his younger sister, the

The Fellows' Garden of Christ's College, where an apparition is seen to cross the lawns on moonlit summer nights

wife of a London physician, and he had grown up to become a tall and powerful man, an unlikely candidate to have followed his father's lead by taking Holy Orders.

In due course Round went to Trinity College to secure a scholarship. It was during this first visit to Cambridge that Round encountered the man with whom he would compete in a number of different spheres for more than twenty years, Philip Collier. Their first meeting took place in the public room of the Blue Boar Hotel in Trinity Street, where the elegant Collier was engaged in lively conversation with the host's daughter, inevitably attracting the attention of other patrons. The two mens' eyes met briefly across the room, a bottle of wine and a pretty woman between them, in what Round later saw as a prophecy of their future relationship.

Round won his scholarship to Trinity, and Collier, it transpired, had won a scholarship to St John's at the same time. Collier was an attractive, well-mannered personality, tall and slim with a rich and distinctive voice and was already making quite an impression on his contemporaries and superiors.

The two men normally had little if anything to do with each other, and it was only when they were both entered for the Bell Scholarship that the pattern of their future, and frequent, academic encounters was established. Round worked hard but without success, achieving nothing more than an honourable mention, whereas Collier was equal first.

This pattern prevailed for a long time. Whenever the two men met in competition, Collier invariably won, more by the intangibles of natural grace and style than by the solid scholarship displayed by Round. The mathematical tripos provided the one occasion for Round's scholarship to triumph over Collier's flare, with the latter being placed several places lower in the honours. Before long, both obtained their degrees and ended their undergraduate careers.

In time, both became fellows of their respective colleges, both were ordained at Ely Cathedral on the same day and both, for different reasons, felt the need for change with Collier resigning from St John's and going to Italy for many years and Round determining to seek office at one of the smaller colleges.

The opportunity of a fellowship soon arose at Christ's, and Round was duly elected. Another vacancy remained to be filled and, at the first fellows' meetings that Round attended, Collier, recently returned from Italy, was proposed. Round felt powerless to intervene as there were no grounds for opposing Collier with his academic record. Thus Collier also became a Fellow of Christ's, just one month after Round. Nevertheless, Round's uninterrupted spell at the college had, by now, given him the edge on Collier academically if not socially, so he was not at all perturbed by Collier's presence.

Four years of gradual consolidation passed, until Round, on long vacation with friends on Lake Geneva, met Mary, Lady Clifford, a widow of some three years, who was in the process of editing her late husband's papers. A little over thirty at the time, she was a beautiful woman, and they became well acquainted before Round returned to Cambridge. They did not meet again for another year, but for the month that followed her return they worked together almost every day before she had once more to go abroad.

Round waited patiently but illness delayed Mary Clifford's return, and it was two years before she arrived back in Cambridge. In the meantime Collier's work had been, in Round's eyes at least, diminishing in quality, but he remained as popular as ever socially. Mary Clifford duly took up residence in Chesterton, a district on the edge of the city centre, and before long Round was again spending much of his time assisting her with her papers. After a year or so, Round had begun to feel that he would soon have to take his chance and ask for her hand in marriage but he looked longingly and in vain for signs that his feelings about her might be reciprocated.

Mary Clifford had to go abroad again for six months, and again Round waited hopefully. But a few weeks after her return, when they were working together in the library one afternoon, a chance remark of hers about Philip Collier being one of her many correspondents shattered any illusions Round may still have had about the potential of his relationship with her. He was devastated. He had instinctively avoided introducing one to the other, and this simple remark left him with a strong sense of foreboding. She explained that they had met in Italy on her last tour and that she had asked him, with a group of her friends, to dine with her. From that day forward, Round's happiness gradually vanished, and he became uncomfortably aware of her growing friendship with Collier.

Then Collier began to change. He became less sociable at the college, entertaining far less than before, and never after nine o'clock. He disappeared most afternoons for an unknown destination and refused to account for his movements. This situation continued for some time before Round had occasion to visit Collier one night and found him sitting limply in a chair barely aware of what was happening. A strong smell of spirits in the room convinced Round that the man was helplessly drunk. Furthermore, both his shoes and clothing were covered in mud as if he had been for a country walk.

Round was puzzled both by the obvious lack of bottles and glasses in Collier's room and by his manner and appearance which would certainly have aroused attention if he had come through the main entrance. A few nights later, while walking in the Fellows'

Garden, Round saw Collier hastening unsteadily across the lawn from a patch of shrubs towards a little-used side-gate that led from the garden and was close to his staircase in the Fellows' Building, just before a light went on in his room. Round later discovered the concealed entrance from Christ's Pieces through the college boundary wall into the patch of shrubbery from which Collier had been seen hurrying.

Outwardly, Collier had changed little and he seemed to spend more and more time with Lady Clifford. One morning in his rooms Collier innocently showed Round some exquisite miniatures of Mary Clifford and himself, each painted by the other in Italy. This, to Round, seemed to doom for ever his chances of courting her, and he became both lonelier and more frustrated by what he saw as the deceit of a secret drunkard.

Within the university at large the Chair of Greek had become vacant. Both Round and Collier were entered, but Round was simply unable to summon the necessary concentration to do himself justice, and this prominent post went, inevitably, to Collier. This was a blow to Round for he knew that his own failed love affair had now caused the loss of the professorship and he had no doubt whatsoever that the exact reverse could be said of Collier.

Round became more despondent. He could not sleep and so prolonged his night-time walks in the garden. One night weeks later at the end of May and in the course of his walk, Round heard the gate from Christ's Pieces shut, followed by the sound of a person brushing through the bushes. It was Collier who stumbled drunkenly out onto the swimming-pool surround and, appearing uncertain as to which direction to take to avoid this natural hazard, swayed unsteadily before lurching back towards the bushes. He lost his footing in a patch of soft soil and, failing to regain his balance in time, fell headlong into the water.

Round had been uncertain what to do but, seeing the man struggling feebly in the water as if dazed, he hurried from his hiding-place and picked up a long, hooked pole which was lying on the bank. As Round turned to offer it to him, Collier was beginning to make his own erratic way to the bank. This enraged Round; the man's good luck was again coming to his rescue, and it looked as if he would actually make it to safety. Round determined that he should not. Whatever good intentions he had felt when he picked up the pole evaporated in his anger and disgust that this drunkard should be allowed to marry the kind and dignified Mary Clifford. A gleam of moonlight shone through the trees onto Collier's upturned face as

Engraving of Philip Collier 'drunk' in his rooms (from A College Mystery*)*

their eyes met. Round stood for a moment with the pole outstretched above Collier's head – and then let it drop. The heavy hooked end hit Collier on the left temple, his head fell back and he disappeared into the water.

That was the last Round saw of Collier and almost the last he heard. Round managed to return to his rooms that night, but fell seriously and inexplicably ill, losing consciousness for several weeks. He recuperated for a year away from Cambridge and when he returned to the college neither Collier nor the cause of his death was mentioned. He presumed it had been regarded as an accident. Nobody suspected the truth.

Round heard once from Mary Clifford soon after the tragedy but did not reply. She died ten years later at the age of forty-five at the house of friends near Nottingham. Within both college and university Round refused advancement, choosing to live as a recluse and continuing to take daily walks in the garden, but only to the end of the great lawn; he would never venture near the pool.

The Coroner's Inquest

A newspaper report was all that survived of the inquest into Collier's death, which took place while Round was unconscious. The body had been found early in the morning by a milkman, not in the pool but on Milton's Walk, a public footpath running alongside the edge of Christ's Pieces next to the college's high wall. It was formally identified by the college's bursar, Dr Caleb Parkins, as that of Philip Collier.

There followed a long debate into the possible causes of death and the character of the deceased. Much water had been found in the lungs and a strange smell, reminiscent of preparations containing alcohol, lingered about the body. There was a deep wound in the forehead, and the man's clothes were wet, as if he had fallen into the river. Witnesses were questioned exhaustively, but the biggest revelation was the testimony of Dr James Simpson, a physician from Edinburgh.

It appeared from his voluntary statement to the inquest that Collier had been assisting Simpson and his colleagues in their early research into anaesthesia and that his friend, Lady Clifford, was also interested in their work. Differing quantities of experimental preparations had been administered on several occasions to Collier, with his full co-operation, to assist in gauging the volumes sufficient for undertaking pain-free surgical operations of varying length.

The coroner was not amused or impressed by this work which both he and the jury regarded as rash, presumptuous and reprehensible. The jury then returned a verdict of 'Accidental death by a blow on the head caused by a fall, resulting in the injuries as described in the medical evidence.' There was no consideration given to the possibility of another more sinister cause or to the involvement of any other parties.

The Other Papers

Goodridge's collection also contained his own notes and Collier's will, made shortly before his death as he knowingly embarked on further dangerous experiments in anaesthesia with Dr Simpson. Five years after Lady Clifford's death, Goodridge wrote that he had met, by chance, the physician who had attended her up to her death. He stated, to Goodridge's astonishment, that her life could have been saved by a single operation carried out under anaesthetic, one that would have been impossible without it.

Furthermore, Collier's interest in anaesthesia had preceded his meeting with Mary Clifford. He had, by the time he met her, stopped taking part in Dr Simpson's experiments because the frequently adverse reactions were making him unwell, but he renewed his involvement as soon as he became aware of her condition and its potential remedy. His selfless determination to sacrifice his own health and, tragically, his life for his beloved Mary were to make him a hero within the college.

As for Round, he had died in obscurity, keeping his grim confession secret for fifty years after his death, and denying himself advancement by way of expiation. He had been chronically mistaken in his judgement of Collier, having prematurely reached his conclusions knowing only half the story and without even attempting to look objectively beyond his own interest at the interests of others.

But was he solely responsible for the death of Collier? How did Collier's body come to be found outside the college walls, on Milton's Walk? Could Collier really have taken himself there with the double impediment of a serious head-wound and the residual drowsiness of recent anaesthesia, or was the evidence given at the inquest as wrong as the jury's verdict? One thing is, of course, certain beyond any reasonable doubt and that is that we could never know the answers to these questions without discussing them in depth with the tall, bent figure in the old-fashioned coat that walks the Fellows' Garden, stopping briefly at the old yew-tree before disappearing once more into the shadows.

Old Hall, Newnham College

Newnham College

The college occupies a pleasant site south of the junction of Sidgwick Avenue and Grange Road in west Cambridge, a few minutes walk from the Backs in the former hamlet of Newnham. To the north of the junction is Selwyn College, and a little to the east is the comparatively recent Arts Faculties site. The area is sufficiently removed from the city centre and from the majority of tourists and casual visitors to retain much of the tranquillity that would have attracted the college's founders in the first place. Newnham was also the first college in this part of the city which now, in addition to Selwyn, accommodates Ridley Hall, Clare Hall, Robinson College and Clare's Memorial Court, as well as the University Library and one of the handful of courts for real tennis in the country.

A Brief History

Newnham College began modestly and experimentally with five young ladies arriving in October 1871 at 74 Regent Street, a dark, gloomy and uninspiring building which had been rented by Henry Sidgwick, a Fellow of Trinity College, as a result of his concern at the lack of opportunities for women at the university. The building was cramped, and the first students were obliged to work at their studies at the same table as they used for meals because the few single bedrooms were just not big enough for desks.

Within four years the college had moved to its permanent home in Newnham, having occupied a series of increasingly larger premises in the meantime as women's higher education became less of an experiment and more of an established fact. By the time the decision was taken to build new premises in Newnham, to be called Newnham Hall, Girton College's new buildings were well under way, but as the aims and methods of the two institutions were to be significantly different, Sidgwick was satisfied that they could co-exist quite happily as they both developed.

When building work started it was to continue more or less uninterrupted until 1910, with the architect Basil Champneys being involved in all the separate projects. Old Hall was completed in the

Henry Sidgwick *(1838–1900), Knightsbridge professor of moral philosophy, founder of Newnham College and the first president of the Society for Psychical Research*

Eleanor Mildred Sidgwick *(1845–1936), second principal of Newnham College and sister of Prime Minister Arthur Balfour*

summer of 1875, ready for the new term in October, and like many of the buildings that followed employed a more delicate and domestic style of architecture than had been adopted by Waterhouse at Girton. The corridor method of access to rooms, first used at Girton, was developed here and eventually resulted in one of the longest continuous corridors in Europe.

Henry Sidgwick's role in founding the college was recognised, albeit at his and his friends' own expense, in 1892 in an obvious and permanent way at the conclusion of a hard three-year campaign to close the intrusive public footpath that ran straight through the middle of the site, between the older buildings. By way of substitution for the lost right of way, Sidgwick Avenue was created at the north side of the site, and Newnham was finally able to claim its privacy.

There were occasional additions to the college, both immediately before and after the Second World War, and a later brief flurry of activity in the 1960s, but although Newnham had received its charter and statutes in 1919 and was able to admit women to the 'titles of degrees' in 1921, its women, like those of Girton, did not become full members of the university until 1948.

The Ghost-hunters

No book about the college ghosts of Cambridge would be complete without reference to Newnham College and its early years, not because of its ghosts for none has ever been recorded there, but because of the involvement of Henry Sidgwick in founding the Society for Psychical Research (SPR) in 1882 and of his wife in the running of it, before she in the fullness of time became the college's second principal.

The future Mrs Sidgwick, Eleanor Balfour, had been born in Scotland in 1845. Her younger brother, Arthur, was to become Prime Minister in 1902 and was installed as the first Earl of Balfour in 1922. Their mother had been interested in the development of women's higher education at Cambridge and when Arthur Balfour completed his mathematical tripos in 1869 the opening of Benslow House in Hitchin, the forerunner of Girton College, was only months away.

Balfour's tutor at Trinity had been Henry Sidgwick who, having introduced him to the lady in charge of the embryonic Newnham, was able to persuade his sister, Eleanor, to subscribe to student bursaries. Eleanor Balfour had already begun to attend spiritualist 'sittings' in London and thus knew Sidgwick in this context as well as in Cambridge. Their mutual interests not surprisingly led in due course to their marriage in April 1876.

Four years later, at the age of thirty-five, Mrs Sidgwick became Vice-Principal of Newnham under Miss Clough, a position which required her and her husband to move into the college itself. She remained in the post until 1882, before handing over to her former secretary, Helen Gladstone, daughter of William Ewart Gladstone, and returning with Sidgwick to their previous home. Aside from her activities at Newnham, Mrs Sidgwick was also assisting Lord Rayleigh, professor of experimental physics, in setting new electrical measurement standards at the Cavendish Laboratory from 1880 to 1885.

Sidgwick himself had long been interested in spiritualism at a time when it was not taken seriously by the scientific establishment. Together with other like-minded colleagues he had begun to sift through reports and evidence from around the world but without any great progress, and so at the beginning of 1882 the Society for Psychical Research was founded with Henry Sidgwick as its first president. The SPR's prime objective as embodied in its constitution was, in essence, to collect every possible scrap of information relating to all aspects of psychical activity so that the assembled data could be rigorously investigated in the hope of arriving at scientifically credible conclusions.

The SPR initially consisted of only 100 members and, although she did not become a member until 1884 for fear of associating the college with what some might regard as a group of cranks, Mrs Sidgwick proved to be an astute and capable administrator who provided considerable support to her husband and his fellow members in processing the mountains of paper that their countless investigations generated.

The council of the SPR contained a number of prominent spiritualists in its early years but their older, quasi-religious approach to the subject did not fit comfortably with the more detached and critical intentions of the scientists, and they soon went their own way. But spiritualism was only one of a number of topics that were under investigation and which included telepathy, the name given to the new field of thought-transference, hypnotism, theosophy, clairvoyance and others.

The study of apparitions featured prominently and became absorbed into the telepathic researches, but in all the fields of study the one thing needed in great quantity was evidence. The general public were invited to submit stories for investigation and did so by the thousand, so much so that the SPR's office sent out over 10,000 letters during 1883 as well as carrying out the many subsequent interviews and site visits.

Eleanor Sidgwick was largely responsible for sifting through the reports and compiling a list of 370 that were worthy of further study. One of these was the story of the ghost at Emmanuel House, Cambridge, which appears earlier in this book and which like many, many more was rejected by Mrs Sidgwick because of the absence of first-hand witnesses to question. Despite the huge workload that the scrupulous search for factual accuracy generated, the SPR continued to solicit even more submissions from the public for the simple purpose of assembling such a large body of evidence that it could no longer be ignored by sceptics.

The society, and its reputation, continued to grow and by 1886 had over 600 members. The Sidgwicks' work for the society also increased, and Mrs Sidgwick became involved in the *Census of Hallucinations* carried out by the SPR, which had begun to show concern in the demands that Newnham placed on her. Its concern was justified because in 1892, when Miss Clough died, Mrs Sidgwick was successfully prevailed upon to take on the role of principal, meaning once more that she, with Henry, had to move back into the college.

Two years later, in July 1894, the *Census*' final report was published, encapsulating findings and accompanying statistics from replies received from some 17,000 people. It was mostly Mrs Sidgwick's work and gives some clue as to the scope of the project and the dedication of its participants. Their work, both at the college and for the SPR, continued unabated until, in 1900 at the age of sixty-two, Henry Sidgwick died of an internal cancer. Eleanor Sidgwick remained Principal of Newnham for another ten years and served as bursar until 1919, before retiring from college life. She was then 74 years of age but had already been the SPR's honorary secretary for twelve years as well as following in her late husband's footsteps by becoming its president in 1908. She retired from the secretaryship in 1932, the society's jubilee year, and died four years later, a month before her ninety-first birthday.

There are two further members of Newnham whose work for the SPR attracted attention, and controversy, at the time. The first is Mrs A.W. Verrall, who taught classics at the college at the turn of the century, and the second is her daughter, Helen, later Mrs W.H. Salter. Mrs Verrall was renowned for her psychic powers in the field of automatic writing – more properly, she was an automatist – meaning that she was able, whilst in a trance-like state and thus unaware of her actions, to write down messages supposedly originating in the spirit world and which could be, for example, in a language unknown to her, from people that she had never met or even heard of.

There were a number of automatists, some of them in the United States and India, who became involved in what were called cross-correspondences. Mrs Verrall had known one of the founders of the SPR, Frederic Myers, before his death in 1901, and she soon began to receive messages from him, or at least his spirit, through the medium of her automatic writing. Unbeknown to her, other automatists in touch with the SPR were also receiving messages from Myers around the same time, and a theory began to emerge that he and other spirits, including Henry Sidgwick, were trying to demonstrate beyond all reasonable doubt that it was possible for the dead to communicate with the living. Mrs Verrall's daughter, Helen, also a student at Newnham, received some of the messages. They were generally incomprehensible, often in Greek or Latin, and only began to make any sense when a group of them, received by different mediums in different places at different times, were put together, translated and analysed at length.

The connections between the messages, known as scripts, were complex in the extreme, with obscure references to ancient tombs and Shakespearean characters, and over a thirty-year period some 2,000 scripts were collected and subjected to detailed study by the SPR. Inevitably, Eleanor Sidgwick was involved and, true to the original intentions of the founders of the SPR, she helped to devise and carry out simple tests to verify the authenticity of self-proclaimed mediums by eliminating any possibility of telepathy with live contacts that would produce misleading, if not completely bogus, results.

The story of Newnham may not reveal any real ghosts but it has the next best thing, a dedicated group of psychical researchers, prepared to limit the chances of ridicule by colleagues and the scientific community, as well as the public at large, by embarking so diligently on rigorous, critical assessments of the mass of information that came their way on a variety of topics that it became difficult for even the greatest sceptic to discredit their work. In so doing they established without doubt the credibility of their own investigations as well as contributing to the future scholarly reputation of Newnham College and its students.

Sidney Sussex College

Sidney Sussex College occupies a city centre site almost midway between the Round Church and Market Hill on the east side of what is now called Sidney Street, to the south of the junction with Jesus Lane, where the high brick wall surrounding the college grounds is at its most imposing and where it faces Trinity College's mid-Victorian Whewell's Court. On its south side the college land includes the commercial properties fronting Sussex Street as it leads into Hobson Street and then on to King Street to the east.

A Brief History

The college was founded in 1594 by the granting of a charter by Elizabeth I, following the bequest of £5,000 and her silver plate by Lady Frances Sidney, Countess of Sussex, who had died in 1589. Sidney's full name is thus 'The Ladie ffrauncis Sydney Sussex Colledge'. The executors of the estate seem to have experienced difficulties in buying the site they wanted because the Franciscan priory standing on it had been given to Trinity College by Henry VIII, following the dissolution of the monasteries, and Trinity was not keen to sell. In the end, a strong letter from Elizabeth I changed Trinity's mind, and work eventually started in 1595 to salvage and repair what remained of the dilapidated buildings, many of which had been dismantled to provide materials for Trinity's own use elsewhere.

By 1600 the surviving parts of the priory's refectory had been converted by Ralph Symons into a two-storey building with a chapel on the ground floor and a library above, and Hall Court, containing the kitchen, the Master's Lodge, the hall and the buttery had been completed to form what collectively are known as the Founding Buildings. Within little more than a decade of its founding, Sidney Sussex's most famous undergraduate was to arrive. Oliver Cromwell came up to Sidney on 23 April 1616, the day that Shakespeare died, but had to leave after only a year to support his family after the death of his father.

The college continued expanding, and in 1628 Sir Francis

The chapel of Sidney Sussex College with its distinctive bell-turret

Clerke's Range was finished. Sir Francis had given money to the college for fellowships and scholarships, as well as for this additional building work which completed Chapel Court, the second of the two three-sided courts that face west towards Sidney Street.

After about 150 years of occasional repairs and minor works, a new chapel was built as the east range of Chapel Court by James Essex between 1776 and 1782. In the early nineteenth century Sir Jeffry Wyatville was given the task of restoring the fine, but deteriorating, Elizabethan buildings. He left the college with the rather unfortunate appearance of a Gothic castle by the addition of many inappropriate features, including a new skin of cement rendering to conceal the alterations to the original red brickwork.

No further building works of any significance were undertaken until the end of the nineteenth century, when the construction of Cloister Court took place to the north of Hall Court. In the early years of the twentieth century the chapel was lengthened and more elaborately decorated and soon after the First World War Garden Court was completed. Other blocks have been developed over the years, the most recent in 1983, but in concluding this brief history it is worth mentioning the strange events that followed Oliver Cromwell's death in 1658.

At the Restoration of the monarchy in 1660 Cromwell's body was exhumed and then hanged. His head was removed from the body and mounted on a pole at Westminster Hall in London where it apparently stayed for twenty years before being blown down in a bad storm. The head, apparently embalmed, then changed hands several times before finally being presented to Sidney Sussex College by Dr H.N.S. Wilkinson in 1960. It was eventually laid to rest in a secret place in the ante-chapel in the presence of the master and two fellows, where its presence is commemorated by a nearby plaque.

The Ghost of Sidney Sussex

The story of the Sidney Ghost is unusual in the context of this book, because the apparition which is recorded occurred comparatively recently, in 1967, and two of the undergraduates present at the bizarre events of that year have been kind enough to provide first-hand accounts of their recollections as the basis for this story.

In 1967 the south wing of Chapel Court stood with its antiquated rooms and creaking staircases virtually unaltered since their construction in about 1630. As with most such 'sets' of rooms, the staircases provided access to rooms which were stacked one upon the other, with anything from two to four rooms per landing, and with no horizontal connection with the sets on other staircases. The rooms concerned were undoubtedly damp and musty as they did not have the benefit of modern heating to dispel their historic 'atmosphere' but were remodelled and refurbished shortly after. Perhaps as a consequence of these various works there have been no further sightings reported in the vicinity of the old staircase 'H' to compare with those that are described below.

It was about 1 a.m. on 1 November 1967, and All Hallows' Eve – more commonly known as Hallowe'en – had technically come to an end at midnight. John Emslie, a third-year student, called on another, Peter Knox-Shaw, but finding that he was not in his second-floor room decided to sit and read quietly as he waited. After a while, he suddenly became aware of a presence in the room which seemed to take the form of a large mouth. Emslie then felt strangely cold and sensed a gripping feeling in his neck. He saw what he described as a vague, emaciated head – not white but pale yellow in colour and not transparent either, but more like an absence of air. The head also appeared to be without ears. Emslie, suitably stunned, left soon after, by which time he had been in Knox-Shaw's room for the best part of an hour.

In the meantime, Knox-Shaw, unaware of Emslie's vision, had returned to his room. As he entered the room he had what he later described as 'a fright'; his hair stood on end, he felt unusually cold and he noticed a strong and peculiar smell, but saw nothing. He must have left his room at this point because he remembers bumping into Emslie almost immediately. Emslie said to Knox-Shaw that he had just told another student, Hugh Evans, about the apparition he had seen in Knox-Shaw's room and then proceeded to describe it graphically. He, like Knox-Shaw, had become aware that the presence was accompanied by a strange smell which was variously described at the time as resembling not only slightly rotten raw meat but also both Spam and Oxo.

The following afternoon on the same staircase, but on a higher floor, there was a further apparition. Mike Howarth's set was on the third floor, directly above Knox-Shaw's. His fiancée, Linda Nield-Siddall from Newnham College, was sitting on her own in the room, apparently unaware of the events of the previous night. It was about 4.30 p.m. and nearing dusk, and Miss Nield-Siddall was, in the words of her fiancé, half-dozing in the gloom.

She looked around and saw a large pale blue and purple eye close to the light switch, between her chair and the door. Her first reaction was that she was seeing spots before her eyes, but at the third glance she became convinced that there was more to it than that. The eye continued to come and go for about ten minutes, at the end of which Miss Nield-Siddall decided to leave since she was understandably becoming increasingly nervous.

There were other experiences recorded by students soon afterwards, including at least one more eye and several reports of unusual coldness, but perhaps the most bizarre scene was enacted when Emslie, Knox-Shaw and Howarth got together to hold a seance in Howarth's room one night. Interest in the paranormal in and around the college was undoubtedly high at the time, and word of their plans seems to have spread well beyond Sidney's precincts.

As the three of them sat at an Ouija board, trying hard to re-create their various experiences, the door to the room opened unexpectedly and to their great disappointment, instead of a dramatic entrance by a multicoloured eye or some other equally exotic and possibly malodorous manifestation, at least twenty members of the Cambridge University Psychical Research Society squeezed in and distributed themselves about the place, ready to examine and attest to any visitation that might have been inclined to put in an appearance. Needless to say, whatever atmosphere the three undergraduates had been able to generate rapidly evaporated, and the seance was abandoned somewhat abruptly.

Two Candidates for the Position

As to the identity of the apparition, Peter Knox-Shaw has suggested two potential candidates.

The first, William Prynne, meets the requirements of the first

***Oliver Cromwell** (1599–1658) – a former student at Sidney Sussex College and later an MP for Cambridge – his head was secretly buried in the ante-chapel of his old college in 1960. (Pastel by Samuel Cooper.)*

sighting because he had had his ears cut off whilst being held in a pillory on Jesus Green, Cambridge. Prynne was a Puritan antiquarian born in 1600 and a graduate of Oriel College, Oxford, who was called to the Bar in 1628. He was outspoken in his views and managed to offend the authorities greatly by writing a series of plays in 1632 that included 'reflections' on the Queen, Henrietta Maria, and for this he was prosecuted, committed to the Tower, fined £5,000, expelled both by Oxford University and by Lincoln's Inn and, as if this was not enough, ordered not only to stand in the pillory but also to lose both ears! However, other than losing his ears in its pillory, Prynne seems to have had no other direct link with Cambridge, and this should perhaps disqualify him from further consideration.

The second candidate qualifies because of his lack of body, at least as far as Sidney Sussex is concerned. It is, rather predictably, Oliver Cromwell, and Knox-Shaw concludes by suggesting that, although the condition and integrity of Cromwell's ears at the time of his burial in the college's ante-chapel are not known, it is nevertheless the sounder attribution.

The story of Sidney's apparitions achieved some local notoriety at the time. It was the subject of an article headed 'Spook or Spoof? Ask Sidney' in the *Cambridge News* the week following the first sightings, which subsequently re-appeared in the college's own Annual in 1989.

The story remains intact to this day, but perhaps the most disturbing aspect of it – at least to the manufacturers of Spam and Oxo – is that not only were their tasty products equated with smells that were 'strange and unusual', but that they were also compared to slightly rotten raw meat!

As Peter Knox-Shaw remarked at the time to the *Cambridge News*, 'One amazing thing is that everybody takes it absolutely seriously.'

Postscript

There is one last story to tell. It concerns one of the older colleges, close to the city centre but not in the natural path of the majority of tourists. The story would be an embarrassment to the college if its name and those of the central characters, some of whom are still alive, were revealed, and so, in deference to their wishes, it must remain anonymous. Nevertheless, it is necessary to sketch out some outline to set the scene for an extraordinary sequence of events.

The college consists of a cluster of largely medieval buildings enclosing two courts, with an entrance squeezed meanly between them that sadly, but typically for this institution, lacks the ornately decorated arms of its founder and is therefore not easy to find, unless it is your home. It has never felt the need to charge the few tourists that, having strayed in error from the main routes, dare to venture through the forbidding oaken doors, because the proceeds would be so small and the costs of collecting them so great by comparison that it is just not worth it. Furthermore, there are extensive landholdings, many of them in the centre of London, which have kept the proverbial wolf a long way away from the college's door for an extremely long time, and no doubt will continue to do so, as they allow the master and the small but select group of fellows that form the college society a pleasantly comfortable and secure existence.

The buildings themselves are nondescript but solidly constructed and painstakingly maintained, a description that might be applied to the fellows themselves, for the achievement of academic distinction was never at the top of the college's list of priorities over the years. There have been successes, of course, but not generally within the public gaze, and certainly not trumpeted from the ancient rooftops in the modern manner of press releases, sound bites and media opportunities. Sporting records have also eluded the college's junior members but they do enjoy one of the finer and more comfortable combination rooms, so perhaps there is just insufficient motivation to leave these pleasant surroundings for the purpose of, as one student put it recently, 'wasting an entire afternoon running around in the freezing cold pushing people over in the mud.'

The Unsuccessful History

A recently arrived Research Fellow, who for the purposes of this story will be known as Spencer, was interested in learning of the college's history although he was a scientist by training and inclination. He discovered that there was no formal college history in the old library or anywhere else for that matter, so on an impulse he resolved to write one himself, as a diversion from the more esoteric worlds he frequented for several hours a day at the lower end of a microscope, snooping on the personal habits of a wide range of micro-organisms.

He approached the master for his consent. The master, like his predecessors, could not see the point of it; after all, the only people likely to be interested in a college history were the members of the college itself, and if they really wanted to know what had happened in the past they had only to ask the honorary librarian who would be sure to give generously of his time in answering their questions, or the master would want to know why. At least that is what he told Spencer. Spencer, not known to take things lying down, argued that that was not the point. Anyway, what would happen when the present librarian was no more, which to one as young as Spencer did not seem to be far in the future, for there was no obvious candidate waiting in the dusty, book-filled wings in the form of an assistant ready at a moment's notice to fill the historical breach. The argument continued, apparently, for some time and was only won for Spencer by his persistence and stubborn refusal to accept defeat.

Spencer was, like many scientists, a computer fanatic. Whatever he started would only get progressed and finished if its needs could be fulfilled by punching away at a keyboard for hours on end. Thus the first items to be moved into the mean and dingy attic room to which he had been directed were his computer, its 'hi-res' colour screen, keyboard and 'mouse'. Clothes, food and all the other irritating paraphernalia for living came a poor second. As for the room, it was at the top of one of the oldest staircases and had been somewhat malevolently allocated by the domestic bursar to Spencer, or so it seemed to other members of the college, considering the dampness which had kept it empty for so long.

Spencer devised a database, into which he would insert all the historical and biographical detail he expected to uncover in the college's archive so that he could sort and shuffle the bare facts before embarking on the narrative itself. The first afternoon's unsystematic digging unearthed some worthwhile bits and pieces of devious politicking from the eighteenth century, and Spencer hurried back to his attic to open the database. He was completing the third entry when, to his surprise, the computer seized up for no apparent reason. He had not been trying anything too electronically ambitious but the screen pointer obstinately refused to obey the mouse's meanderings on its special mat, and the machine just would not respond to any of Spencer's irritable key-commands.

A restart was the only answer, but it meant that the entries that Spencer had already completed once, but had not saved, would be lost and therefore have to be re-entered. Spencer pushed the power switch off and then on, and the familiar melodic cross between a bing and a bong signalled the machine's return to life. He sat looking as the simulated desktop appeared on the screen with its collection of equally artificial files and folders, neatly arranged in rank and file, but then something at the bottom of the screen caught his eye.

An unusual icon, a small graphic image representing a file or document, had appeared. Spencer did not recognise it from any of the programs he regularly used, and its title, which was 'Untitled', gave nothing away either, but its appearance was vaguely reminiscent of an old heraldic device, as if from a coat of arms. He moved the pointer over this new icon and, full of curiosity, double-clicked the mouse button to open the file. He could hear the computer's hard disk grinding away in its box beneath the monitor and, all of a sudden, the screen was filled with a white page, displaying a message that he did not at first take in. More grinding came from the computer's box, and the machine seized again.

Forgetting his momentary irritation at another 'crash' and refraining for once from the usual futile keystrokes and accompanying expletives, Spencer concentrated on trying to remember the message. He was not completely sure but he thought that it had been 'Bewarre for hiftory will itfelf repeat.' He restarted again and waited while the desktop sorted itself out. The heraldic icon was no longer at the bottom of the screen.

Spencer was puzzled by this and began to wonder if he had imagined the whole episode. He was sure he had not but there was nothing to show for it so he carried on with his work. A week or two passed before he had a chance to spend another afternoon rummaging in the archive and, again, there were some interesting documents for him to work through, making notes of references, dates and people long since departed whose contribution to collegiate life had been meticulously recorded for occasions such as this. Spencer returned to his room full of enthusiasm and opened up the database.

He had been typing away for some time when, in the process of entering brief details about a master who had died over two hundred years ago, the machine seized. Spencer cursed loudly, but at least he had saved the data entries a few moments before and would not lose as much time as he had on the first seizure. Without thinking, he restarted and wandered off to switch the kettle on. By the time he returned to look at the screen the mysterious icon 'Untitled', not seen since the previous incident, had reappeared at the bottom edge of the simulated desktop. Spencer hesitated and then decided to print out a copy of the screen as it stood – at least he would be able to consult a colleague or two about the likely software that had generated it. He keyed in the necessary commands and waited for the printer to respond. It did not, but the computer did, by seizing up again. This was becoming tedious.

Restarting the machine and watching its every electronic move very, very carefully Spencer waited for the desktop to appear. To his surprise, the icon was still there, so he tried opening it up. The screen filled quickly with a bright white background and a message flickered briefly before, yet again, the machine ceased to respond to Spencer's frantic manipulations. But at least he had been prepared for a quick scan of the message and, this time, he had no doubt about its content. It said, quite simply, 'Seek not, and you fhall not find, or fuffer either.'

Spencer recognised the f's as the initial s's of the eighteenth century printer – at least his superficial historical forays had taught him that – and pondered his next move. He did not bother to restart there and then for he knew that the icon would have disappeared. In Spencer's mind there was no immediate sense to be made of the two messages, even when they were read together, but he would have been lying if he had tried to tell anyone that he was not a little disturbed. Somehow the idea of a college history did not carry quite the same interest as it had, but he felt trapped by his own enthusiasm. He could not very well abandon the project without losing face with the master whom he had badgered into sanctioning it in the first place and who held the key to his advancement within the college society, but what else could he do?

Spencer tried to put these seizures behind him and thus immersed himself in his real work with an intensity that surprised him even more than it did his colleagues. But late one afternoon, as he was walking out of the college library, he almost managed to knock the master over as he turned towards his staircase. Spencer mumbled a few elementary courtesies, but as he tried to sidle away the master enquired after the college history and its progress, for he was now looking forward to presenting an inscribed copy to the Vice-Chancellor before the start of the Long Vacation.

Spencer steeled himself, lied through his teeth and affirmed that he had recently come across some unexpected and intriguing documents that might make interesting reading if he could only interpret them properly. The master, deciding to take that as a positive sign, wandered off towards the lodge for tea. Reluctantly, the research was started again, the database brought back into operation and the archive plundered for more detail.

Things went well for a while, and Spencer almost, but not quite, forgot about the earlier teething problems with the computer. Then one sunny spring afternoon a few weeks later Spencer came across a faded yellow pamphlet in a box that he must have missed on a previous search. He opened it carefully and soon became absorbed by the macabre story of an eighteenth-century master who had died in peculiar circumstances. Apparently one of the college servants found his body hunched over a folio of documents that he had been consulting as part of the preparation of a college history, but there were no signs of anything as suspicious as a struggle, so his death had been ascribed to an apoplectic seizure on the death certificate, even though there was no evidence of past ill health to support it. Spencer made copious notes about the pamphlet, its writer (a contemporary Fellow) and the attitude and room in which the body had been found in the Master's Lodge, as well as other relevant facts, dates and names, and hurried back to his attic.

The disturbing new information that he had uncovered was duly added to the growing database, without further incident, and before long Spencer was able to begin writing the manuscript of his history. Conscious that time was running short, as were his literary skills, he resolved to ask the master for advice on the draft manuscript and, as he had expected, the master was in turn irritated and then flattered at the request. Spencer printed out a draft of the first few chapters as soon as he could and left it with the master's secretary the following morning, before pedalling off to the laboratories for another morning's invasion of bacterial privacy at the bottom of a microscope.

Being completely absorbed in his own thoughts to the exclusion of all other stimuli was a common enough experience for Spencer so, even if he had noticed the small, hushed group hovering outside the entrance to the Master's Lodge as he returned from the laboratory, it would not have occurred to him to ask what they were doing there. Consequently, he walked straight past their blank, silent stares, across the court and up to his attic. He switched on his computer as he shut the door and was momentarily confused by an unusual sound, just like an ambulance siren, before the familiar bing-bong signified the completion of the computer's self-checking procedure. Then he saw, appearing on the screen for the first time in weeks, the old heraldic device that formed the icon labelled 'Untitled'. Unable to resist, he double-clicked the mouse button and waited for the inevitable crash as the document opened. The screen went blank, then white, and a message appeared, but not quite as he had expected.

The message read: 'You chofe to difregard the warning. Be it on your head alone.' Spencer looked at the open attic window and then back to the screen. The message was still there, the computer had not seized up, and Spencer, more than a little agitated, decided that he had to shut it down, but he could not. Nothing happened as he pushed the various keys, nothing at all. Except that he became aware of noise coming through the window from the court below and the increasingly loud sound of a siren – he was sure it was an ambulance – as it seemed to come closer.

In one of those quantum leaps of comprehension that people are prone to once in a while, Spencer suddenly understood what was happening. He rushed out of his room, down the staircase and across the court to the group he had passed and ignored a few moments before. As he tried to push past them, the bursar, standing at the front door to the lodge, restrained him. He started to tell Spencer what had happened just as the ambulance team arrived in the court with a stretcher, but Spencer knew already without having to be told.

Spencer knew that the master had been found by one of the college servants, hunched over a folio of documents that he had been consulting as part of the preparation of a college history – Spencer's history. He knew in which room and in what position the body had been found and he knew that it had been a massive stroke that had caused the master's death, because that is what the death certificate would say.

He knew these things because he had read them in the old yellow pamphlet that he had found in a box in the college archive. Spencer knew that an apparition had visited itself upon his predecessor, warning him not to write the history, a warning that had been ignored then as he had ignored it now and with the same tragic consequences.

It will come as no surprise to learn that Spencer abandoned work on the history and soon decided that his fortune, good or bad, lay elsewhere. As for the college, it neither has a history nor does it want one, for the newly installed master has, like his predecessors, read in private the ancient parchment note, handed down in a much-sealed envelope from one to the next, that confides a strange secret about the college's founder and issues with it a warning too appalling to reveal. Only two men have chosen to disregard it.

Bibliography

Historical Background

Cambridge, ed. Rebecca Snelling (Basingstoke, Automobile Association, 1988).

Feiling, Keith, *A History of England* (London, BCA, 1973).

Jeacock, Janet, *Cambridge Colleges* (Norwich, Jarrold Publishing, 1994).

Jeacock, Janet and Jeacock, Michael, *The City of Cambridge Official Guide* (Norwich, Jarrold Publishing, 1994).

Kent, Sally, *A Jarrold Guide to the University City of Cambridge* (Norwich, Jarrold Publishing, 1992).

McWilliams-Tullberg, Rita, *Women at Cambridge* (London, Victor Gollancz, 1975).

Rawle, Tim, *Cambridge Architecture* (London, Trefoil Books, 1985).

Reeve, F.A., *Cambridge* (London, B.T. Batsford, 1976).

Stubbings, Frank Bedders, *Bulldogs and Bedells – A Cambridge ABC* (Cambridge, F.H. Stubbings, 1991).

Taylor, Christopher, *Cambridgeshire and Mid Anglia* (London, Willow Books, 1984).

Trevelyan, G.M., *English Social History* (BCA, London 1973).

University of Cambridge History, various authors (London, F.E. Robinson & Co., 1899 *et seq.*).

Ghosts, Apparitions and the Paranormal

Ellison, Arthur, *The Reality of the Paranormal* (London, Harrap, 1988).

Out of this World (London, Macdonald & Co., 1989).

Smith, Stefan, 'Ghost Town' in *Varsity* (Cambridge, Varsity Publications, 17 March 1989).

Underwood, Peter, *The Ghost Hunter's Guide* (Poole, Blandford Press, 1986).

The Colleges – listed in the order in which they appear in the book:

Corpus Christi College

Bury, John Patrick, *The College of Corpus Christi and the Blessed Virgin Mary* (Cambridge, Corpus Christi College, 1952).

Smyth, C.H.E., 'The Corpus Ghost' in *Corpus Association Letter* (Cambridge, Corpus Christi College, 1986).

Girton College

Bradbrook, M.C., *'That Infidel Place' A short history of Girton College 1869–1969* (London, Chatto & Windus, 1969).

Megson, B. and Lindsay, J., *Girton College 1869–1959* (Cambridge, W. Heffer & Son, 1959).

Clare College
Forbes, M.D., *Clare College 1326–1926* (Cambridge, 1928 and 1930).
Paulopostprandials, ed. Owen Seaman (Cambridge, 1883).

Emmanuel College
Gauld, Alan, 'The Emmanuel House Ghost' in *Emmanuel College Magazine* (vol. XLIX, 1966–7).

Jesus College
Gray, Arthur and Brittain, Frederick, *A History of Jesus College Cambridge* (London, Heinemann, 1979).
'Ingulphus' (Gray, Arthur), *Tedious Brief Tales of Granta and Gramarye* (Cambridge, W. Heffer & Sons, 1919).

Peterhouse
Winstanley, D.A., *Unreformed Cambridge* (Cambridge, Cambridge University Press, 1935).
Anon., *An Account of The Late Dispute between the Bishop of Ely and the Fellows of Peterhouse etc.* (2nd edition, 1788).
Anon., *The Gentleman's Magazine* (vol. 59, p. 957, 1789).

St John's College
Stevenson, Geoffrey, 'A Visit from the Other Side in a Township near Banbury in 1706' in *Cake and Cockhorse* (vol. 12, no. 2; Banbury, Banbury Historical Society, 1992).

Christ's College
Baker, A.P., *A College Mystery* (Cambridge, W. Heffer & Sons, 1923).

Newnham
A Newnham Anthology, ed. Ann Phillips (Cambridge, Cambridge University Press, 1979).
Hamilton, Mary Agnes, *Newnham An Informal Biography* (London, Faber & Faber, 1936).
Sidgwick, Ethel, *Mrs Henry Sidgwick – A Memoir* (London, Sidgwick & Jackson, 1938).

Sidney Sussex College
Wyatt, T.S., In *Sidney Sussex College Annual* (Cambridge, Sidney Sussex College, 1989).
Anon., 'Spook or Spoof? Ask Sidney' in *Cambridge News* (Cambridge, Nov. 1967).